Portable Operating

for **Amateur Radio**

Everything you need to get on the air in the great outdoors!

Stuart Thomas, KB1HQS

Production:
Michelle Bloom, WB1ENT
Sue Fagan, KB1OKW—Cover Art
Jodi Morin, KA1JPA
Maty Weinberg, KB1EIB

Front Cover: Jerry Clement, VE6AB, operates from the summit of a peak in the Canadian Rockies. [Photo by Jerry Clement, VE6AB]
Front Cover Inset: The author, Stuart Thomas, KB1HQS. [Photo by Stuart Thomas, KB1HQS]
Back Cover: Ruth Willet, KM4LAO. [Photo by Stuart Thomas, KB1HQS]

We strive to produce books without errors. Sometimes mistakes do occur, however. When we become aware of problems in our books (other than obvious typographical errors), we post corrections on the ARRL website. If you think you have found an error, please check **www.arrl.org/notes** for corrections. If you don't find a correction there, please let us know by sending e-mail to **pubsfdbk@arrl.org**.

Contents

Preface

"Life is Either a Daring Adventure or Nothing." — *Helen Keller*

"How hard could it possibly be to climb a 4000 foot summit in Maine?"

I asked myself this question in my quest to activate my first Summits on the Air (SOTA) location. The summit in question, West Peak on the Bigelow Mountain range in northwest Maine, proved harder to climb than I anticipated.

After consulting a topographic map and grabbing my hiking gear, I hastily assembled a 2-meter Yagi antenna out of miscellaneous parts worth about $3. Along with the antenna, I grabbed my handheld VHF radio, set the frequency to 146.520 MHz, and off I went.

After an arduous climb, I camped out on the ridge line that night, and the next morning made my way to West Peak summit. While eating a quick breakfast, I got my radio, logbook, and antenna out of my pack and started calling CQ SOTA. The abrupt change from hiking using my gross motor caveman skills to the fine motor skills of operating a radio proved challenging — an interesting mental shift that is not often experienced in daily life. The view from the summit was overwhelming and mesmerizing at the same time. After an hour I made several 2-meter contacts, some with stations more than 80 miles away. Not bad for 5 watts and a Yagi made out of some acrylic tubing, piano wire, and coax terminated with alligator clips.

That activation solidified my quest for more hiking and radio operations in the backcountry. The skills required include navigation, self reliance, low-power operations, and setting up temporary antennas in awkward windy locations. I was hooked for life.

Sharing my passion and enthusiasm with others makes the experience much more enriching. I wrote this book to motivate both newcomers to ham radio and long-time licensed operators to explore the world of portable operating. This book is written as a how-to-guide to get you started operating portable in fun and new locations other than the home ham shack.

So get off the couch, turn off the TV (or internet), grab your radio gear, and head outside. Make the world your ham shack!

Writing a book is not a solo endeavor. Like hiking solo in the wilderness or sailing offshore, it is always good to have support. My father, the Old Man, introduced me to the world of Amateur Radio. Many thanks also to my amazing wife for her support in my quest to write this book, and to my trail dog who is my long-time hiking companion. He stood watch many times as I made contacts.

I'm grateful to ARRL for allowing me the opportunity to share my portable operating skills and techniques with the amateur community. My editor, Mark Wilson, K1RO, helped guide me through the publishing process with his enduring patience.

There are also many more people to thank who have helped me in many ways: Johnny Twist, K5ACL; Peter Kobak, KØBAK; George Burger, WØPHX; Ruth Willet, KM4LAO; Bill Jourdain, AB4BJ; Emily Saldana, KB3VVE; Tim Watson, KB1HNZ; and the Wireless Society of Southern Maine (**www.ws1sm.com**). Also thanks to National Park Service Rangers David Lassman and Yusuf Abubakar at the Thomas Stone National Historic Site in Maryland for their hospitality and support of the hobby during my many visits to that interesting site.

Finally, I would like to thank everyone who has answered my CQs that radiated from summits, national parks, lighthouses, islands, rowboats, and urban parks. Without all these contacts, I couldn't have gained the portable experience needed to write this book.

73,
Stuart Thomas, KB1HQS
March 2018

About the Author

Stuart Thomas, KB1HQS, was exposed to Amateur Radio from an early age thanks to his father (the "Old Man") who also is a lifelong Amateur Radio operator.

After high school, Stuart received the rank of Eagle Scout, attended college, and pursued a career in the maritime and adventure industries. Interlacing his love of the outdoors with adventure, he obtained his commercial captain's license and spent considerable time offshore working as a professional sailor onboard tall ships and private yachts. Later on, while living on the coast of Maine he worked as a marine electronics technician and boat builder. This experience gave him the opportunity to partake in several large-scale yacht refits in famous Maine boat yards rich with maritime boatbuilding history.

Over the years he has obtained numerous certifications, including PADI dive instructor, Wilderness First Responder, EMT, and SAR Rescue Team member. Until recently, he served as a volunteer and board member on a search and rescue team in Maine where he was involved in several searches for missing weekend warriors and an Appalachian Trail through-hiker, which resulted in one of the largest SAR searches in Maine's history.

As an avid hiker himself, he has hiked at the Philmont Scout ranch, numerous sections of the Appalachian Trail, and several 4000-foot peaks

throughout the United States including Utah, Maine, New Hampshire, and Virginia. His love of hiking with portable radios has led him on the quest for SOTA Goat, a coveted Summits on the Air (SOTA) activator award.

Stuart holds an Amateur Radio Extra ticket and has been licensed since 2001. He has written several articles on portable operating for *QST*, as well as a section on portable operating for the *ARRL Operating Manual*. His interests include QRP, portable radio operating, and building antennas.

In 2016, Stuart was the top activator in the ARRL's National Parks on the Air (NPOTA) year-long event, with more than 500 activations. Stuart also enjoys helping to mentor operators new to the hobby and teaching others outdoor skills.

Like many in the Amateur Radio community, he hosts a website (**kb1hqs.com**) and YouTube channel (**KB1HQS**), where he shares videos of his radio adventures and reviews Amateur Radio equipment.

Stuart can be found on variety of social media platforms including Twitter, Pinterest, and Instagram (under his call sign). He can be reached via e-mail at **kb1hqs@arrl.net**.

About the ARRL

The seed for Amateur Radio was planted in the 1890s, when Guglielmo Marconi began his experiments in wireless telegraphy. Soon he was joined by dozens, then hundreds, of others who were enthusiastic about sending and receiving messages through the air — some with a commercial interest, but others solely out of a love for this new communications medium. The United States government began licensing Amateur Radio operators in 1912.

By 1914, there were thousands of Amateur Radio operators — hams — in the United States. Hiram Percy Maxim, a leading Hartford, Connecticut inventor and industrialist, saw the need for an organization to unify this fledgling group of radio experimenters. In May 1914 he founded the American Radio Relay League (ARRL) to meet that need.

ARRL is the national association for Amateur Radio in the US. Today, with approximately 170,000 members, ARRL numbers within its ranks the vast majority of active radio amateurs in the nation and has a proud history of achievement as the standard-bearer in amateur affairs. ARRL's underpinnings as Amateur Radio's witness, partner, and forum are defined by five pillars: Public Service, Advocacy, Education, Technology, and Membership. ARRL is also International Secretariat for the International Amateur Radio Union, which is made up of similar societies in 150 countries around the world.

ARRL's Mission Statement: To advance the art, science, and enjoyment of Amateur Radio.

ARRL's Vision Statement: As the national association for Amateur Radio in the United States, ARRL:

- Supports the awareness and growth of Amateur Radio worldwide;
- Advocates for meaningful access to radio spectrum;
- Strives for every member to get involved, get active, and get on the air;
- Encourages radio experimentation and, through its members, advances radio technology and education; and
- Organizes and trains volunteers to serve their communities by providing public service and emergency communications.

At ARRL headquarters in the Hartford, Connecticut suburb of Newington, the staff helps serve the needs of members. ARRL publishes the monthly journal *QST* and an interactive digital version of *QST*, as well as newsletters and many publications covering all aspects of Amateur Radio. Its headquarters station, W1AW, transmits bulletins of interest to radio amateurs and Morse code practice sessions. ARRL also coordinates an extensive field organization, which includes volunteers who provide technical information and other support services for radio amateurs as well as communications for public service activities. In addition, ARRL represents US radio amateurs to the Federal Communications Commission and other government agencies in the US and abroad.

Membership in ARRL means much more than receiving *QST* each month. In addition to the services already described, ARRL offers membership services on a personal level, such as the Technical Information Service, where members can get answers — by phone, e-mail, or the ARRL website — to all their technical and operating questions.

A bona fide interest in Amateur Radio is the only essential qualification of membership; an Amateur Radio license is not a prerequisite, although full voting membership is granted only to licensed radio amateurs in the US. Full ARRL membership gives you a voice in how the affairs of the organization are governed. ARRL policy is set by a Board of Directors (one from each of 15 Divisions). Each year, one-third of the ARRL Board of Directors stands for election by the full members they represent. The day-to-day operation of ARRL HQ is managed by a Chief Executive Officer and his/her staff.

Join ARRL Today! No matter what aspect of Amateur Radio attracts you, ARRL membership is relevant and important. There would be no Amateur Radio as we know it today were it not for ARRL. We would be happy to welcome you as a member! Join online at **www.arrl.org/join**. For more information about ARRL and answers to any questions you may have about Amateur Radio, write or call:

ARRL — The national association for Amateur Radio®
225 Main Street
Newington CT 06111-1494
Tel: 860-594-0200
FAX: 860-594-0259
e-mail: **hq@arrl.org**
www.arrl.org
Prospective new radio amateurs call (toll-free):
800-32-NEW HAM (800-326-3942)
You can also contact ARRL via e-mail at **newham@arrl.org**
or check out the ARRL website at **www.arrl.org**

Chapter 1

Overview

George, WØPHX, operating from South Mountain off the Mormon Loop Trail in Arizona.
(Courtesy George Burger, WØPHX)

Amateur Radio is a vast hobby that includes a multitude of different niche hobbies. Portable operating is one of them. Amateur stations traditionally have been associated with a table full of gear at an operator's home. In recent years, that has changed with the increasing popularity of operating portable away from the home ham shack.

A New Generation of Equipment

In the past, radio transceivers were large, heavy, power hungry devices. Newer technologies such as surface mounted components, digital signal processing (DSP), and software defined radio (SDR) have created a new generation of compact, portable radios with low power requirements that are well suitable for portable field use. Although battery-friendly QRP CW radios have been around for a long time, today's radios cover multiple bands and modes and have many of the features found on desktop radios.

Elecraft's KX3 is very popular among portable operators because it covers 160 through 6 meters with 15 W output, has low current drain, and operates on all modes. It has a built-in CW keyer, DSP filters, antenna tuner option, and many other features — yet fits in the palm of your hand and weighs less than 2 pounds.

The rapid development of portable consumer electronics has been made possible, in part, by advances in battery technology. Modern lithium-ion (LiFePO$_4$) batteries are light weight, compact, and long-lasting — ideal for powering a portable amateur station for many hours.

The recent development of good performing, full-featured, small and lightweight transceivers and batteries, along with an increase in organized outdoor radio operating activities, clubs and programs, has spurred more amateurs to venture into portable operations.

Challenges at Home

Along with radio technologies, social and cultural changes have occurred in the hobby. More hams are living in dense urban areas, with high noise levels and restrictions that prohibit or severely limit antenna set-ups. Those factors can make ham radio operation from home very difficult.

Some amateurs living outside urban areas contend with Home Owner Associations (HOAs) and deed restrictions or covenants that are not radio friendly. This has resulted in many amateurs leaving the home station and going outside to operate portable. Backyards, state and national parks, mountain summits, islands, and other locations are all being used as temporary radio shacks.

Dave, W4JL, enjoys portable operating while using his truck as his base of operations and antenna support. (Courtesy David Ledford, W4JL)

Rex, KE6MT, proves that you can set up a portable station anywhere — this is near the summit of Mt Whitney in California. (Courtesy Rex Vokey, KE6MT)

The 2016 ARRL National Parks on the Air operating event found Kelley, KS6Z, operating from Gates of the Arctic National Park and Preserve in Alaska. (Courtesy Kelley Shelley, KS6Z)

Portable Operating With Other Activities

Another reason to operate portable is that the skills and techniques can be applied to public service and communications during emergencies. The ability to transport, set up, and get a station on the air quickly in austere conditions lends itself well to the emergency preparedness field. Portable operators have the ability and practical experience to improvise

Paul, W6PNG, enjoys a mix of ham radio, hiking, and incredible scenery. (Courtesy Paul Gacek, W6PNG)

Portable operations can take place from urban locations as well. Supporting an antenna and finding a quiet spot to set up can present some challenges, though.

antennas and solve technical problems with limited resources available. The portable operator also becomes very familiar with his or her gear, and this familiarity proves invaluable when operating under difficult situations.

Portable radio operations can also carry over into other hobbies such as hiking or visiting national or state parks, and urban areas. Possessing flexibility, innate knowledge of their equipment and the desire to set up in new or unusual locations creates a challenge that many operators thrive on.

Who does portable operating? The only criteria are being a licensed Amateur Radio operator and having the desire to operate portable. Portable operators use HF and VHF bands, as well as SSB, FM, CW and digital modes. There is something for everyone, no matter their license class or interests.

This book was written for the licensed Amateur Radio operator and serves as a how-to-guide on portable radio operations. The book is divided into 10 chapters, finishing with an appendix.

Chapter 1: Overview
Chapter 2: Types of Portable Operating
Chapter 3: Organizing and Carrying your Equipment
Chapter 4: Radios for Portable Operating
Chapter 5: Power Sources
Chapter 6: Portable Antennas
Chapter 7: Propagation and Spotting
Chapter 8: On the Air Activities
Chapter 9: Accessories and Tools
Chapter 10: Logging Contacts
Appendix: Online Resources

Chapter 2

Types of Portable Operating

Amateurs enjoy many different types of radio operating. For the purposes of this book, we will consider two types: mobile and portable operating. Within the amateur community there is often a gray area defining what constitutes mobile and what constitutes portable Amateur Radio operations.

While the FCC does not define either term in the 47 CFR Part 97 Amateur Service rules, in years past there was a requirement for stations to identify themselves as mobile (/mobile) and portable (/portable), among other designations. While this is no longer the case, operators will often voluntarily use these designators to indicate their particular activity to others while on the air.

Mobile Operation

First we'll discuss mobile operating, and for this book we will define that as *operating from a vehicle while in motion*.

What defines a vehicle? The list is long and varied and includes the following examples: car, airplane,

Bill, AB4BJ, enjoys operating from his SUV. His consistently healthy signals during his 280 National Parks on the Air (NPOTA) activations in 2016 prompted a number of questions about his antenna system — and he was glad to share the details. (Courtesy Bill Jourdain, AB4BJ)

Bob, N4CD, has been an avid mobile operator and county hunter for decades, and he has transmitted from every county in the United States. An avid CW operator, Bob can often be heard operating CW while in motion.

boat, canoe, kayak, recreational vehicle (RV), tractor-trailer, train, bicycle, motorcycle, snowmobile, hot air balloon...and the list goes on. Hams show a lot of imagination in this area!

The other factor defining a mobile station is that *the antennas are attached to the vehicle, and the radio is contained inside the vehicle.* If the antennas and/or radio are set up outside of the vehicle, that is often considered portable operation.

Mobile amateur stations range from a simple handheld or mobile VHF/UHF FM transceiver and magnet-mount antenna, to a multi-band or high-power HF setup. Hams have operated mobile from 160 meters through UHF, although 40, 20, and 2 meters and 70 centimeters are probably the most popular. While voice modes (SSB and FM) are most popular, some amateurs have developed the skills for operating CW from their vehicles while in motion.

Jerry, VE6AB, operates HF through UHF on a number of modes from this very well equipped mobile station. (Courtesy Jerry Clement, VE6AB)

We'll cover equipment and antennas in later chapters. You can read more about setting up a mobile station in the *ARRL Handbook*, online from the ARRL website (**www.arrl. org/mobile-stations**), or a very comprehensive collection of articles, information, and links about mobile operating from HF through UHF by Alan Applegate, KØBG (**www.k0bg.com**).

Ruth, KM4LAO, operating from a well-equipped station in a vehicle. (Courtesy Ruth Willet, KM4LAO)

Safety First

While operating mobile, there are a couple of considerations for successful and safe operation. Proper planning for the radio installation needs to follow the correct guidelines, including choosing the correct power wire size and fusing the power leads appropriately for the

The KB1HQS bicycle mobile setup includes a battery powered HF transceiver and magnetic loop antenna.

radio you plan to use. All equipment, including remote control head and the main radio chassis (if separate), needs to be fastened securely and not interfere in the event of airbags deploying or cause injury in a vehicle collision.

Along with airbag issues, mounting radios on the dash can obstruct the driver's view. In recent years, attention has focused on use of electronic devices (especially handheld devices) in vehicles and distracted driving. A number of states have hands-free and distracted driving laws that may impact Amateur Radio mobile operation. It is your responsibility to ensure proper installation and legal operation of your radio gear in a mobile setup. One source of information about distracted driving laws is the Governors Highway Safety Association (**www.ghsa.org/state-laws/ issues/Distracted-Driving**).

Boats and Airplanes

While mobile operations are typically associated with passenger cars and trucks, there are other types of mobile operations including aircraft and marine or maritime. (*Maritime mobile* is a designation indicating operation in one of the maritime regions — generally outside of national boundaries, in international waters. Marine mobile is an unofficial description indicating operation from a vessel. That can include operating from a watercraft on inland rivers, lakes and other water bodies, or offshore but within US territorial waters.)

Bil, KD6JUI, enjoys operating 6 through 80 meters from his kayak. (Jeff Brook, photo)

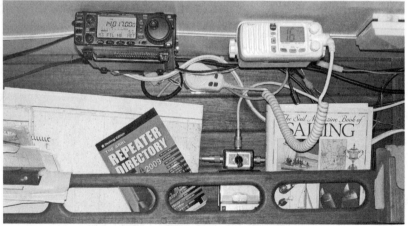

Joel, W1ZR, installed his HF/VHF amateur transceiver near his marine radio. The antenna is a wire supported by the backstay. (Courtesy Joel Hallas, W1ZR)

Operating aeronautical mobile first requires permission of the pilot before you can transmit. Operating at altitude can give you wide coverage, especially on VHF where your line of sight (LOS) is magnified by the height. While not as common as other mobile operations, an aeronautical radio experience can be exciting and can induce fun pileups.

Marine and maritime mobile is very popular among boaters. That can range from bringing a handheld along on a canoe or kayak, to a VHF or HF setup with a good antenna on a larger motorboat or sailboat. Those who venture offshore use not only marine SSB radio, but amateur HF SSB radio as well. The amateur Winlink network and specialty nets such as the Maritime Mobile Service Network (**www.mmsn.org**) on 14.300 MHz and Hurricane Watch Net (**www.hwn.org**) on 14.325 and 7.268 MHz during weather events are crucial communication links for boaters, both near shore and offshore. Amateurs should use courtesy while operating near these new frequencies. More information on marine mobile operating may be found at **www.arrl.org/marine-mobile**.

The National Weather Service offers forecasts via radiofax (weatherfax) on a number of HF frequencies, although they are not in the amateur bands. An SSB receiver (such as the general coverage receiver in your HF transceiver) and a computer running some readily available software are required. More information is available online from **www.nws.noaa.gov/os/marine/radiofax.htm**.

When you operate maritime mobile in international waters, your FCC amateur license still applies. If you operate from a private vessel, you will need written permission from the owner and captain prior to bringing your gear onboard and operating. If your ship is docked in another country's territorial waters, you need to be aware of the appropriate rules for reciprocal operating privileges in that country. Due to the nature of the travel, maritime mobile operation requires diligence in making sure you are following correct procedures for the vessel you are on, the country you may find yourself in, and any local laws. Check out the ARRL website for more information: **www.arrl.org/maritime-mobile-operation-in-international-waters**.

Portable

Portable is defined for this book as operating away from your fixed home station, often with a temporary setup. This setup includes bringing your own transceiver and antennas, and usually a power source. The antenna installation is often quickly assembled and temporary. Portable also includes operating from vehicles that are stopped, often using external antennas that would prevent the driver from moving the vehicle without disassembling the antenna. An antenna on a mast secured with guy wires is a good example.

There are many different types of environments where you could operate portable. Examples include the following:

- Mountain summits
- City, state, and national parks
- Backyard setups for testing purposes
- Emergency Operation Centers (EOCs)
- Hotels while traveling
- Mobile stations that are stopped with antennas set up externally

The key factor for all of the above locations is that they are temporary and are away from the home station. Even operating portable from your backyard while close to home is an excellent way to test out your equipment before heading to more remote locations. Forgetting a key piece of equipment such as coaxial cable or a charged battery can make all the difference in a successful portable experience.

Portable operation can be as simple as a QRP radio with self-contained battery pack and a wire thrown in a tree. Or it can be as complicated as a Field Day setup with generators and multiple antennas. Perhaps the biggest challenges are coming up with an effective portable antenna that covers the band(s) you enjoy, as well as a practical power source that will run your radio for the desired operating period. We'll cover these topics in detail in later chapters.

Location, Location, Location

Operating either mobile or portable, you can find yourself in locations that have challenges and special requirements that you need to consider. These locations include rural or remote locations and urban areas.

George, WØPHX, enjoys hiking and operating from remote summits as well as from parks. He can be heard activating summer and winter from his native Minnesota, as well as when traveling. (Courtesy George Burger, WØPHX)

(L-R) Bert Dumont, KB1ZLV, Dakota Dumont, KB1YYC, Frank Krizan, KR1ZAN, and Tim Watson, KB1HNZ, operating from atop Mount Washington in New Hampshire. (Courtesy Tim Watson, KB1HNZ)

Rural Locations

The first challenge in operating from rural or remote locations is often just getting to the location. Although we have come to rely on the use of smart phones and GPS navigational aids, they don't always get the job done in rural areas. Depending on the part of the country you find yourself in, you may find it helpful to carry backup paper maps (or charts if you are on the water) to supplement the electronic tools.

A good hardcopy resource for the rural operator is the *DeLorme Atlas & Gazetteer Paper Maps* series of books (**buy.garmin.com/en-US/US/p/575993**). Each book covers a single state or two adjacent states and includes both road and topographic maps with latitude and longitude. If you find yourself traveling rural roads, hiking trails, or locating lakes to

When hiking off the beaten path, a topographical map can provide valuable information about terrain, access roads, streams or lakes, and other natural features.

set up a portable shack, the *DeLorme Atlas i*s an excellent guide to have with you.

Here are a few other useful resources:

• **www.heywhatsthat.com** — a handy site to use from summits to identify other mountains

• **www.gaiagps.com** — Gaia GPS, an offline GPS mapping software app

• **www.nps.gov/subjects/digital/nps-apps.htm** — the official National Park Service app

• **www.fs.fed.us/visit/maps** — the official US Forest Service map portal

• **www.blm.gov/maps** — the official Bureau of Land Management map portal

As of this writing in 2018 there is wide cell coverage in the United States, but there are still many rural areas that lack decent coverage. Shenandoah National Park in Virginia is a good example of an area with spotty cellular coverage. While coverage is good on the tallest features in the park, there are still parts that lack decent coverage. That's also true in vast areas of the western US, as well as sparsely populated northern New England, to name a couple of other examples. Hams from urban areas tend to take reliable cell coverage for granted, but it's another world out in rural areas. One place to find cell coverage maps for a number of carriers to research portable locations is OpenSignal (**opensignal.com**).

Set a Good Example

The author found Ranger Yusuf Abubakar at the Thomas Stone National Historic Site in southern Maryland to be very friendly and helpful during multiple activations. Ranger Abubaker was interested in ham radio and even got on the air.

While selecting a site to operate, it is your responsibility to know the local city, state and federal laws regarding access. Take for example, the national parks, historic sites, and monuments throughout the United States. While they are federal properties managed by the National Park Service (NPS), our FCC license does not exempt us from following all of their regulations and policies. Checking in with the park rangers can confirm what is required. Some parks may have specific areas they would like you to operate from or restrictions on the type of antenna you can set up. Some may even require permits in order to operate your station. The above applies to any city or state-owned park or other facility that you operate from as well. Part of being a considerate operator is following the laws and representing the hobby to the public in a positive image.

Another time when projecting a good image is very important is operating from popular mountain summits. While we may have strong passion for Amateur Radio, others who are visiting the site may not know about Amateur Radio or share the same passion about our hobby. If you are operating in an area with hikers or other visitors present, use earphones to keep the noise to the minimum. Keep coax feed lines and antennas (including guy wires) out of the way so they don't become tripping hazards. Don't block popular views or hiking trails with your station setup.

At popular locations consider setting up at one of the more remote parking areas to reduce the possibility of interfering with other visitors. Here, Bob, W9LSE, found a nice spot at Zion National Park. (Courtesy Bob Seaquist, W9LSE)

When I go to activate Summits on the Air (SOTA) summits, I often go early in the morning before other people arrive. If other people are present, I will find a spot nearby that is out of the way and not impact the outdoor experience that other visitors are trying to enjoy.

When operating from summits, I often get inquisitive looks and questions along the lines of "What exactly is it that you are doing?" I look at this as an excellent opportunity to educate people about Amateur Radio. Recently I made up a QSL-like card that I can hand out to them that includes information about the hobby of Amateur Radio, and the URL for my website where they can find more information.

Next, there is the issue of radio frequency interference (RFI). This is a problem one would expect only in urban areas, but I have encountered noise and interference even in some of the more remote areas. The only way to determine if RFI will be an issue at a particular site is to set up your station and try it.

This is the QSL-like card that the author hands out to visitors who are interested in what he is doing during activations.

Always act with the utmost courtesy and respect all local rules and other visitors. This sign indicates that the park is a quiet area (so headphones would be a good idea) and that no stakes or poles are to be driven into the ground.

Urban Locations

On the opposite end of the spectrum, urban areas have their own issues in operating a radio. Urban denotes cities, which means lots of people, myriad rules and congestion, potential interference to and from your equipment, and a general lack of personal space to set up your station and antenna.

The first issue is your selection of the particular location in an urban area. If you are operating from your car and are using a mobile antenna mounted on the car ("self-contained"), you may be able to keep a low profile — assuming you are parked in a legal spot. Once you decide to set up equipment or antennas external to your vehicle, you need to determine if you have permission from the landowner (or park). In urban areas, there will often be more than just local laws that you need to observe. There may be not only city, but also state and federal laws to observe regarding access and acceptable activities.

Operating in urban areas can include severe interference from power lines, subways, trains, commercial vehicles, industrial equipment, neon signs, and countless other potential sources. Also, strong commercial

Pete, KØBAK, operated from one of the most extreme urban locations activated during National Parks on the Air — the stoop of the Peterson House, part of the Ford's Theater National Historic Site in Washington, DC. (Paul Stoetzer, N8HM, photo)

Mark, K1RO, activated several sites in Manhattan using a battery powered QRP radio and magnetic loop. Operating from a park bench at the Stonewall National Monument, with this simple setup he was able to work across the US and into Alaska, as well as a couple of European stations. He was traveling with Alec, W2JU, who had a similar setup and similar results. (Courtesy Alec Berman, W2JU)

transmitters in the area may cause interference. While operating mobile/portable in the Washington, DC metro area, I find that the noise level doesn't decrease until I get onto the interstate beltway. Locations inside the beltway are often unusable due to the interference from high noise levels.

Interference can occur on the transmitting side as well. Using 100 W and the appropriate antenna in the right location can cause RFI to nearby electronics as well. During National Parks on the Air (NPOTA) in 2016, hams operating from a stoop at the Ford's Theater National Historic Site in Washington, DC inadvertently set off a fire alarm with their transmitter. You can't always tell what you are going to interfere or interact with in an area with so many electronic devices present, however do your best not to cause issues for others.

Another urban issue is personal security, especially in major cities. While operating in cities, it is easy to develop "tunnel vision" from focusing on working contacts and tuning out the surrounding environment. Headphones or earbuds can also decrease your situational awareness. If operating from your car, be sure to have your doors locked and windows rolled up.

Using expensive electronics and lack of situational awareness can make an Amateur Radio operator an easy target for harassment and possible theft. Also be cognizant of leaving radio gear in your vehicle while parked. Cover or hide your gear when not in use. Your personal safety and gear are a personal responsibility to take seriously.

Paul, W6PNG, operating from the Golden Gate National Recreational Area overlooking the Golden Gate Bridge. (Courtesy Paul Gacek, W6PNG)

While amateurs love to share their passion with the hobby, our presence in an urban area may be viewed by the general public as "suspicious activity" and attract unwanted attention from the local residents and even law enforcement. Carrying a laminated copy of your FCC Amateur Radio license may help alleviate any concerns law enforcement have about what exactly it is you are doing.

During NPOTA in 2016, I activated LBJ Memorial Grove National Historic Site in Washington, DC, and park police stopped by to inquire about my operation. Presenting my state-issued identification along with my FCC license (and an ARRL NPOTA brochure) helped reduce the tension and educate the officer about my operation. While ultimately they did ask me to leave, which wasn't a problem as I was wrapping up my activation anyway, presenting a federal license does give you some credibility.

Sensitive Areas

So we have discussed areas that are available to operate portable, but what about areas where you shouldn't operate? For example, sensitive areas such government and military locations should be avoided unless you have permission from those responsible for that location.

Businesses and landowners may also object to you operating on their private property and/or business location. Holding an FCC Amateur Radio license does not preclude you from observing private land ownership laws or following the rules. While the airwaves may ignore land boundaries, your physical presence should not unless you have secured permission first.

Outside of the US, you will need to follow the laws regarding radio receiving and transmission in that country, and you may need to obtain a license from the host country if there is no reciprocal operating agreement with the US in place. ARRL has a concise web page that can assist you with discovering what you need to operate outside the country. See **www. arrl.org/us-amateurs-operating-overseas**.

Selecting a Site

We have talked about various portable operating locations in general. Now let's discuss a good procedure to research and select a specific site for portable radio use. To prevent wasted time and frustration, research your location *before* leaving home.

I start with a generic web search and look for information on the site itself. I use Google Maps to look at topographic and satellite views, and street view if available. Satellite views are helpful in that you can see features that may not otherwise be visible on standard street maps. Note that the satellite pictures for the site you are researching may be out of date depending on how recently the images were made.

Another excellent online resource is the Gmap4 web application (**mappingsupport.com/p/gmap4-free-online-topo-maps.html**). This free online application offers enhanced Google maps and a large variety of topographic maps from other sources. You can also download these maps and routes for your GPS navigation device. For those not using a traditional handheld GPS device, you can download maps of the area using Gaia GPS (**www.gaiagps.com**), which is an app for iOS and Android devices that allows for using a variety of detailed maps while offline.

Nick, KC1DKY, operating from the Boston Common. His battery powered 100 W transceiver and "hamstick" dipole mounted on a sturdy tripod generate a fine signal from an urban location.

Ultimately it depends on what type of electronic device(s) you are using (if any).

For hiking and off-road trails, I print a hard copy of my route. While GPS devices and phones are great resources, unlike paper maps they can fail right when you need them the most. And as noted before, cell coverage may be spotty, eliminating the opportunity to download a different or expanded map if needed.

With all the maps and satellite views collected, now take a good look at the site and check for hazards that may cause radio issues. Examples include overhead power lines (not antenna friendly), nearby power stations, commercial transmitters, and any other safety or interference issues. Using Google satellite views and street views can give you good insight to the location you have selected and may point out hazards not otherwise seen on a topographic or street map.

Now that you are familiar with the general area, you can use the internet to see who has operated from the location you have selected and perhaps learn of any issues they may have encountered. Various outdoor radio operating organizations such as Summits on the Air (SOTA), Islands on the Air (IOTA), Parks on the Air (POTA), Worldwide Flora and Fauna (WWFF), and so on, often have websites or Facebook pages where amateur operators post short reports or photos regarding their experience at a particular location. SOTA is particularly good in this regard. Check out this example Mt. Katahdin Activation Report at **www.sota.org.uk/Summit/W1/AM-001.**

Don't discount non-amateur sites either. Hiker and off-road vehicle websites also have extensive information regarding many locations. Summitpost is one example (**www.summitpost.org**).

Activation reports and other helpful information are available on the SOTA website. Here is the page for W1/AM-001, Mt Kathadin in Maine.

Weather and Propagation

With the operating location scouted out, next I check the weather and propagation forecast. Good propagation and good weather are both essential to the success of a portable operation. For online weather information, I often check the National Weather Service website at **www.weather.gov**. A good resource for propagation forecasts and other information is a web page run by Paul Herman, NØNBH at **www.hamqsl.com/solar3.html**.

What if you are on a multi-day trip and have no internet access?

You can get local weather from NOAA on VHF frequencies: 162.400, 162.425, 162.450, 162.475, 162.500, 162.525, and 162.550 MHz. Most of the popular 2-meter and dual-band FM handheld amateur transceivers have weather channel reception built in.

You can get propagation reports via HF radio from WWV/WWVH on 2.5, 5, 10, 15, and 20 MHz. The propagation forecast is announced at 18 minutes past each hour for WWV, and 45 minutes past the hour for WWVH. If you want to use this resource, it's a good idea to familiarize yourself with the terminology (A Index, K Index, and so on) and what they mean in relation to what you hear on the air. More information about WWV may be found at **www.nist.gov/pml/time-and-frequency-division/radio-stations/wwv**. A number of good articles about radio propagation are available from the ARRL website at **www.arrl.org/propagation-of-RF-signals**.

Before heading out on a hike, it's always a good idea to check the National Weather Service website for current conditions.

Other Considerations

The next step is to consider what frequencies you will operate, how much power you plan to use, and what type of antennas you will set up. The location will often determine what kind of antennas you can use. Some locations may limit you to only a mobile antenna, while others allow for antennas to be strung in trees. In many parks, it's forbidden to drive tent stakes into the ground for mast guy wires or ropes, so improvising using heavy weights or water bottles to anchor guy lines may be required.

Also be sure to determine whose property you will be setting up on and if you need permission or a permit. As discussed previously, you need to abide by all rules, whether you are setting up on public property such as a park, or privately owned land.

Don't forget your family at home, especially if you are going into remote locations. Leaving a safety sheet indicating where you are going and what time you should return is smart pre-planning and will be very

The author's e-mail newsletter about his upcoming activations and other topics of interest to portable operators.

handy in the event you encounter problems. The HikerAlert Emergency Alert App (**hikeralert.com**) is one resource that can help.

Now it's time to get the word out using social media to publicize your operation. Using the internet to advertise your upcoming trip and letting chasers know to be on the lookout for you can make the difference between a successful and non-successful trip.

There are several methods that I use, starting with my e-mail newsletter. Over the years I have accumulated an e-mail list (with permission from each person on that list) of hams interested in my activations. Periodically I send out a newsletter about my recent trips as well as upcoming activities. While you can send just a basic e-mail, you will get a better response using a newsletter client such as Revue (**www.getrevue.co**) or MailChimp (**mailchimp.com**).

After sending out an e-mail, I post on Facebook (both my personal page and specialized group pages), Twitter, and the appropriate websites such as SOTA (**www.sotawatch.org**), POTA (**parksontheair.com**), or WWFF (**wwff.co/agenda/**), depending on the type of event.

Now that the word has been spread about your upcoming trip, it's time to gather all your equipment. What is the best way to store, organize and transport your radio equipment?

Chapter 3

Organizing and Carrying Your Equipment

In this chapter, we will explore organizing and packaging the equipment you'll need for a successful activation. Later chapters will talk more about radios, antennas, and accessories.

You don't want to bring too much equipment (things you won't need), especially if you're hiking into a remote location, but you also cannot afford to forget a key item either. You really need to think beforehand about everything you will require for a particular setup and be sure that you have packed it. Having a printed checklist that you can verify prior to leaving home is key in not forgetting any crucial piece of equipment and saving yourself a lot of frustration and wasted time.

You will also need to organize your gear so that it is easy to set up and operate. Time is limited for many activations, so you want your station to go together as quickly as possible. You also want it to be convenient to operate, and not hard to assemble or awkward to use.

Equipment

Equipment for portable radio operations can be divided into two categories: non-radio gear and the radio gear itself.

Non-radio gear includes everything you need to get you and your

Outdoor oriented websites are a good resource to research the non-radio aspects of portable operation. As you venture further from civilization, it becomes more important to become knowledgeable about outdoor equipment and techniques. The Ten Essentials page on the REI Co-op website is a great place to start.

radio to the operating location. If you are hiking, for example to a SOTA summit, the non-radio requirements are much more important. You should have all the equipment you need to be self reliant, including the 10 essentials — things like food and water, map and compass, adequate clothing, lighting, and so forth. There's a great discussion of these essentials on the REI Co-Op website and I strongly encourage you to take a look (**www. rei.com/learn/expert-advice/ten-essentials.html**).

Here are some good sources for information and equipment you'll need to be safe and successful outdoors.

Outdoor Gear Forums
- WhiteBlaze — **www.whiteblaze.net**
- Backpacking Light — **www.backpackinglight.com**

Outdoor Gear Stores
- REI Co-op — **www.rei.com**
- Backcountry — **www.backcountry.com**
- Sierra Trading Post — **www.sierratradingpost.com**
- L.L. Bean — **www.llbean.com**

The rest of this chapter will discuss the radio aspects.

Organizing Your Radio Gear

One of the most vexing issues for portable operators is how you will organize and transport your gear. There are two approaches on how to do this: self-contained and modular (see the sidebar, "Self Contained vs. Modular").

The first way is to have a self-contained kit where all the radio interconnects and power are permanently connected. An example is a go-kit. Go-kits are often installed in hard-sided, weather resistant or waterproof cases that contain the radio, tuner, and any

This self-contained go-kit was the author's first attempt at packaging and transporting a portable station. It included everything to get on the air, but ultimately proved too heavy and unwieldy for operating away from a vehicle.

Self Contained vs. Modular

Self Contained

Pros
- Quick to set up
- Turn on, ready to operate
- Simple setup due to less gear
- More capability (more modes, higher power)
- Less chance of forgetting a key part (antenna coax, tuner, etc) as everything is contained inside the case
- Hard weather resistant or waterproof case to protect expensive gear
- Store gear in same location to increase familiarity and ease of use

Cons
- Often bulky and heavy; can't transport very far on foot
- Cost
- May require lots of power to operate depending on gear energy requirements
- Equipment may be more fragile out of its protective case
- Not easy to exchange parts without some disassembly

Modular

Pros
- Lightweight
- Can carry on back (when using a backpack) or by hand
- Can easily swap out different parts or components as needed
- Possible lower power requirements (or portable power)
- Due to smaller setup, may cost less (depending on gear)

Cons
- Depending on complexity of setup, may take some time to assemble
- Low power (QRP) or if high power (100 W), shorter times to operate depending on power source
- Possibility of forgetting a key piece of gear (eg. coax, microphone)

Johnny, K5ACL, operating with his low-power HF portable station that's transported in a soft-sided go-bag. (Courtesy Johnny Twist, K5ACL)

Self-contained go-kits are very popular with public service operators, since they need to be ready to deploy at a moment's notice. Here, Chris, KC9CRE, is operating during an ARRL Amateur Radio Emergency Service (ARES) exercise involving a nuclear power plant in Wisconsin. (John Wagner, KB9ULF, photo)

other auxiliary gear needed to get on the air. Pelican cases, sound equipment cases, and even ammo cans can be used and modified for radio gear go-kits.

When you are building a go-kit, there are several considerations because of the small, enclosed working space. One is heat management. A case that lacks ventilation can lead to overheating radios and accessories. Installing fans or removing rear panels to allow air flow is important in heat management. Another overlooked issue is operator ergonomics. When you set up your case, verify that you have easy access for VFO tuning and other radio functions. Make sure that you can easily plug in headphones or swap computer connections if needed. Sometimes radios will get mounted such that there is no easy access when setting up for operating.

A Modular Approach

With a modular gear organization, the radio and accessories are transported separately and require connecting coax, power, and other cables upon arriving at the site. A modular gear setup gives the operator the flexibility to add or subtract equipment as needed, depending on your operating objectives and environment. Some examples:

• You may be planning to operate HF only — why carry VHF gear too?

• For a long backcountry hike, you probably want the lightest possible equipment configuration, whereas operating from a picnic table near your car means you can bring more radio and battery.

• A temporary setup at a park will differ from one at an Emergency Operations Center (EOC).

Having the flexibility to modify your setup quickly can be helpful depending on your needs. Each piece of gear may have its own case, or no case at all. However, without cases, you must be more careful to prevent damage.

The author now prefers a modular approach, with gear stored and transported in multiple small bags and assembled on-site. Modules are chosen according to the bands and modes to be used, antenna(s) to be used, and the type of site to be visited. Top row, left to right: wire antenna launcher, coax, Nanuk 905 waterproof case, Wolf River Coil antenna and paracord, AlexLoop magnetic loop. Bottom row, left to right: Osprey Kestral 48 pack, Bucket Boss Extreme Hopalong Tool Tote, Garmin Bag, Pelican Urban Elite Camera Pack, Swiss Gear Laptop Backpack, and PackTenna and SOTABEAMS antenna masts.

Cases for modular organization of your gear can vary from small waterproof Pelican cases to larger bags such as backpacks. I organize my portable radio gear using a tiered system:

1) Main radio bag: HF radio, battery, coax, and primary antenna

2) Computer bag: radio accessories including interfacing cables, manuals, and laptop

3) Alternative antennas/extra feed line bag

4) Tool bag

Considering your radio gear has to be assembled for operation every time (unlike a self-contained go-kit), having your gear stored in an organized and consistent manner is important in making sure you have everything you need.

If you're interested in learning more about the gear I use and how I package and transport it, check out my website: **kb1hqs.com/2018/01/19/gear-series/**. I also have a YouTube channel where I discuss portable operating, outdoor activities, and other related topics. (Go to **www.youtube.com** and search for KB1HQS.)

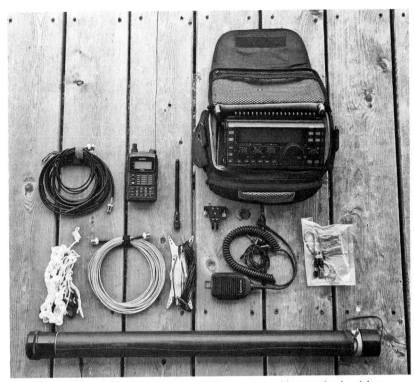

Here is the author's lightweight, compact gear bag for a portable operation involving a hike. It includes an Elecraft KX3 low power transceiver with battery, mic, and CW keyer paddles; a Yaesu FT1DR VHF/UHF handheld; PackTenna multiband wire HF antenna; VHF antenna in a tube; and all needed cables and rope.

Checklist

What is the best way to organize your gear? Do you really need a checklist?

Before I started using a checklist to verify that I had all my gear, I attempted a SOTA activation in Shenandoah National Park. Upon reaching the summit, I realized I had forgotten my coax for the end-fed antenna that I planned on using for the activation. Luckily for me it was a very short hike back to the car to retrieve it. Don't come up shorthanded at your operating site — use a checklist.

A checklist should be organized in a logical manner and include categories for everything you need to operate. Don't forget often overlooked accessories such as radio manuals, adapters, or coax jumpers.

Another good reason to have a checklist is to verify the status of the

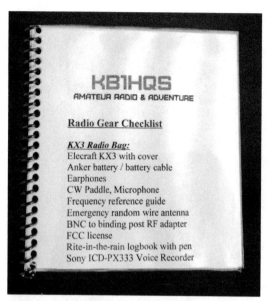

Developing (and using!) a checklist is key to making sure you have *everything* needed to get on the air in the field. Forgetting something as small as a coax jumper or adapter can scuttle your operation before it has even begun.

batteries and operation of your equipment prior to leaving home. Along with power status, I will also verify that all my equipment is in proper working condition before heading out.

With my modular setup, I utilize a physical tagging system to prevent leaving items that are out of my bags, such as batteries that are currently charging or being used elsewhere. Often I will take out my laptop to enter logs and forget to return it to my laptop bag. I use a paint stick with a red embroidered tag attached as a quick visual flag reminding me that an item is not currently in the bag and needs to be added before leaving home.

Other Equipment Considerations

Label all your gear bags and boxes with an easy-to-read ID tag with your name, address, and phone number. Considering the cost of your gear, don't forget to take pictures of equipment for insurance purposes (such as the ARRL Equipment Insurance plan) in case of damage or theft.

While not legally required, it's a good idea to include a laminated copy of your FCC Amateur Radio license with your radio. If you're approached by law enforcement or other officials questioning what you are doing, being able to produce a federal license may help alleviate any concerns and explain your actions.

A paint stick with a red embroidered tag provides a quick visual reminder that an item has been removed from an equipment bag.

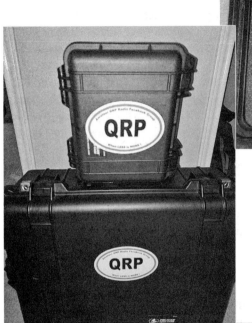

Johnny, K5ACL, has a couple of different Pelican hard-sided cases for storing and transporting gear. The smaller case has a low-power HF transceiver and accessories, while the larger case has a 100 W HF transceiver, battery and cables. (Courtesy Johnny Twist, K5ACL)

Environmental/Travel Hazards

Most radio gear is not well suited to the harsh outdoor environment. Dust, moisture, mud, snow, and other environmental conditions can damage or even destroy your valuable electronics. Waterproof, crushproof hard cases are a good way to protect your radios. I've used a variety of waterproof hard cases from Pelican (**www.pelican.com**), including their very rugged Storm Cases, and think they are a good way to go. Another source for rugged cases is the Nanuk line, available from DX Engineering and other sources.

For cases that are sealed from the atmosphere, don't forget to add rechargeable desiccants to keep the moisture levels low during long term storage. If I have been operating in temperatures with wide variations (hot and cold), I will often remove my radio from the case once I return home and allow it to stabilize to room temperature before returning it to the sealed case.

You should also consider a small unused paintbrush or photographer's dust brush to wipe accumulated dust and dirt off your radio. The soft bristles work well to get into the crevices and tight spots. If your radio is not stored in a waterproof case, adding a heavy duty trash bag to use as a rain cover can be helpful, especially in the field.

Traveling with Your Gear

For the most part, you will probably be operating close to home or driving to your site. If you're flying, there are some additional considerations.

For air travel, TSA regulations must be followed in transporting your gear on a plane, especially if you are bringing batteries. Rules regarding batteries are detailed and can be found here: **www.faa.gov/about/ office_org/headquarters_offices/ash/ash_programs/hazmat/ passenger_info/media/Airline_passengers_and_batteries.pdf**.

If carrying your gear onboard, having a copy of your license with your equipment may help your progress through security if TSA has questions. Also, be aware that antennas may give you increased scrutiny because of how they may appear in security scanners.

Depending on your final destination and radio setup requirements, it may make more sense to ship your radio gear to the location where you will be staying using a commercial shipping service and bypass the airlines all together. The cost may be higher, but it may be less stressful. If you do ship equipment, be sure to add insurance and pack it securely to increase your chances of having your equipment arrive safely.

A backyard picnic table is an ideal place to practice setting up and using your portable station. You'll find out quickly if you are missing anything. While the station is set up, be sure to make some contacts to confirm that your antenna is radiating and that other stations will be able to hear you. (Courtesy Bill Jourdain, AB4BJ)

Another option is contacting amateur operators in the area that you are traveling to and setting up a joint operation or asking to borrow gear. Clubs in the area may be another resource.

Practice

So you have accumulated all the gear you think you need to operate portable. Before heading out to a remote area, try setting up your portable station in your backyard or at local city park. Verify that you have everything needed and that your gear works correctly. This 30-minute exercise can save you a lot of grief later on when you travel a significant distance to operate.

Chapter 4

Radios for Portable Operating

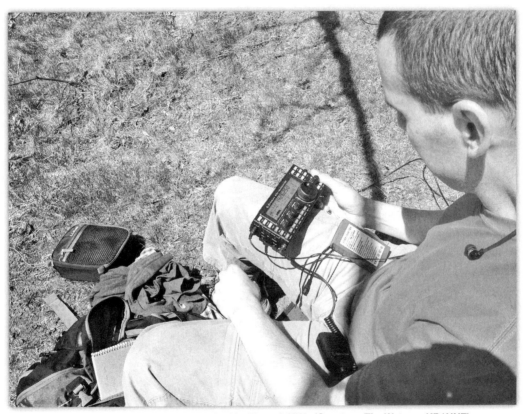

Ryan, KB1YTR, operating 20 meter QRP with his Elecraft KX3. (Courtesy Tim Watson, KB1HNZ)

The transceiver is the first component needed to operate portable, and it is one of the most discussed items for portable radio operations. In years past, portable operators have had a very limited selection of radios for portable operation. Most radios were too big and heavy, or required too much power to be practical for operation in the field.

As technology changed with the introduction of digital signal processing techniques to replace hardware functions, along with surface mounted components, radio transceivers have shrunk to a truly portable size with a myriad of features unheard of even 10 years ago. Today there are a lot of choices, and the radio you select will depend on your budget, operating needs, weight/power requirements, and modes desired.

What's Best?

The question most often asked is, "What is the best radio for portable work?" Just like choosing a radio for the home station, there are many variables that need to be considered before that question can be answered.

The best radio for one person may not be the best fit for others. Everyone will have different operating styles, preferences, budgetary restrictions and other factors. The most important factor is defining what type of operating you plan on doing and the environment you will be in. Someone operating QRP in the Arizona desert will have different requirements from a 100 W station in the Canadian Arctic.

For our purposes, there are two broad categories of transceivers — radios designed specifically for portable or mobile use, and radios designed for home station operation but with features that make them suitable for portable use.

Let's first look at radios that are designed for portable or mobile use and that are available new as of this writing in early 2018. Please note that these are just some examples I am aware of, and this is not an exhaustive list.

Low Power Portable HF Transceivers

- Elecraft KX2 and KX3
- LNR Mountain Topper MTR3B, MTR4B, and MTR5B
- Yaesu FT-817ND and FT-818
- YouKits HB1B

These radios have lower power requirements and weigh less than their desktop counterparts, and they lend themselves to battery operation. Some, like the Mountain Topper series and YouKits HB1B series, are CW-only and cover a limited number of bands, while others cover many bands and modes.

Elecraft's KX2 is a 10 W radio that covers 80 through 10 meters and operates SSB, CW, AM, and digital modes. It's very small and can be powered for several hours from its internal battery. A paddle for the CW keyer attaches to the case. Its bigger brother, the KX3 shown in the title photo, adds 160 and 6 meters and operates at 15 W output.

The Mountain Topper MTR5B from LNR Precision is a CW-only transceiver for 40, 30, 20, 17, and 15 meters. It produces 5 W output with a 12 V dc supply, and will work with as little as 6 V (2 W output).

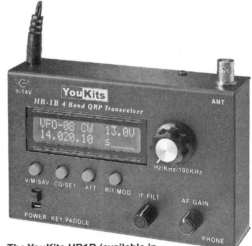

The YouKits HB1B (available in the US from Vibroplex) covers the 40, 30, 20, 17, and 15 meter bands and operates CW only. It can be powered from an internal battery or an external 9 to 14 V supply. Power output is up to 5 W with a 13.8 V supply.

All Band, 100 W Portable/Mobile HF Transceivers

- Icom IC-7100 and IC-7300
- Kenwood TS-480SAT
- Yaesu FT-450D, FT-857D, FT-891, and FT-991A

These radios fit the criteria for portable or mobile use, but some are not advertised primarily for portable or mobile operation. Also, there are likely other all band, 100 W transceivers that portable operators use that are not on the list. And of course all of these radios can be used as home station radios as well.

Icom's IC-7300 is a relatively compact 100 W all-mode transceiver for 160 through 6 meters. It is popular for home station use as well as portable operation.

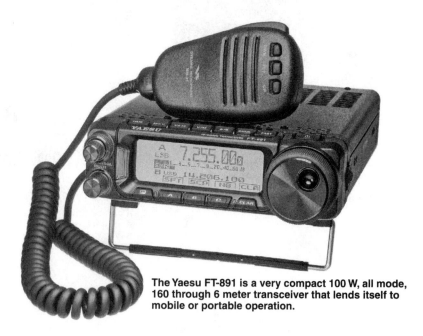

The Yaesu FT-891 is a very compact 100 W, all mode, 160 through 6 meter transceiver that lends itself to mobile or portable operation.

Larger Home Station Radios

Radios that you would typically find in a home station are larger in size and weight, and they have higher power requirements. For home station use, transceivers are rarely moved once installed. The size and weight factors are not a concern, while performance and features are emphasized. Of course this does not mean that home station rigs, particularly those that operate from a 13.8 V dc supply rather than ac mains, can't be moved from the shack temporarily to be used outdoors. For those who are not sure and just want to give portable work a try, this may be a good way to get started. It is up to the operator to decide how much effort is feasible to move gear from home to the field.

While all of the radios listed in the portable/mobile categories can be used in a home station, not all home station radios can be used portable. Ultimately it depends on your operating location, how far you have to carry your radio, and what power is available on site. A Field Day event with generators for power and operating locations a short distance from the car can allow for large home station radios that require 120 V ac supplies. Someone with a radio mounted on a bicycle or a station carried in a backpack will have different requirements.

Portable refers to portability, and high weight and large size are contrary to that idea.

Kenwood's TS-590SG is an example of a home station radio that is small and light enough to be used in the field. It covers 160 to 6 meters with 100 W on all modes.

What to Look For

What variables should you consider when choosing a portable radio? To select a radio for the field you need to ask yourself several questions.

1) How do you plan to carry your gear in the field, and how far will you be traveling?

You may be carrying your gear from your car to a picnic table at a park. Or you may be carrying everything in a backpack over 20 miles in hilly terrain. Obviously given these two scenarios, your weight and size requirements will differ. The backpacker will primarily focus on weight, while the park operator will focus more on transmit power and convenience.

Pete, KØBAK, assembled this "NERD Wagon" for urban activations during National Parks on the Air. Built on a heavy duty garden cart, it easily transports a complete HF station including transceiver, 500 W solid-state amplifier, batteries, mast, and hamstick dipole antenna. The cart doubles as a support for the antenna, making the whole station self-contained and non-invasive. (Courtesy Peter Kobak, KØBAK)

If you're operating near your car, the size and weight of your station equipment is limited only by how much you feel like carrying the short distance. If you're operating in an urban environment with a lot of equipment, a hand cart may be useful.

For those carrying their gear farther than half a mile, a backpack to comfortably carry everything will become a necessity. Many people carry too much gear. As you spend more time operating portable and gaining experience at your particular operating location, you'll come to a better understanding of what gear you truly need. As mentioned in the previous chapter, testing your setup in your backyard or at a local city park can give you a quick idea of what works and what doesn't. It is also useful to find out what pieces of gear you are missing.

2) How much power do you plan on running?

Those running QRP or low power output levels will have different battery/power-source requirements than those running 100 W or more. How much time you plan on operating will also determine your battery/power requirements. You can find more details on this topic in the **Power Sources** chapter.

3) What modes and frequencies do you plan on operating?

The simplest radios are CW only, but a number of the radios listed above operate on all bands and modes. Operating more than one band means adding antennas, or using a multiband antenna. For CW, you'll need to add a paddle, and maybe a keyer. For SSB, you'll need to add a microphone or headset. Digital modes require a tablet or laptop, increasing the complexity and weight factors for an operation.

4) What does your budget allow you to spend on a radio, and what support exists if you have issues?

People often fixate on the initial cost of a product, but consideration should be given for how much support exists from the manufacturer and the availability of repair parts and warranty service. Dealing with an established manufacturer with US sales and support teams increases your odds in after-purchase support. Also be aware that over time, manufacturers discontinue their products and the parts needed to repair them. For those who prefer to repair their own radios, the lack of available repair parts can create issues if something breaks.

5) Antenna selection and antenna tuners.

What type of antenna will you use with your radio? If you're operating with low power or in an area with antenna restrictions, this may influence what type of radio you purchase. Are you using a resonant or non-resonant antenna? Do you need an antenna tuner to make everything work correctly? Some radios have internal tuners while others require an

Portable antennas are often a compromise and may not present low SWR on all desired frequencies. Some transceivers have antenna tuners built-in, but they have limited range. An external antenna tuner such as the MFJ-939 offers a greater tuning range and may be an asset with less-than-perfect antennas.

external tuner. An internal tuner means fewer wires and less complexity, while an external tuner may have a greater matching range. See the **Antennas** chapter for more details.

6) Look to others who have a similar operating style and see what radios they are using.

Find other portable radio operators and see if you can get an on-the-air demo of their radio. If that's not feasible, ask what they like about their radio, and what could be improved.

Clubs are another resource for you to meet local hams with a variety of rigs. Check out the ARRL Club Search page online at **www.arrl.org/find-a-club**.

QST Product Reviews are a trusted source of information and test results for most recent transceivers. ARRL members have access to past reviews online (**www.arrl.org/product-review**).

Online reviews are another source of opinions on various radios. A popular site is eHam (**www.eham.net/reviews/**). There's also a wealth of information available on YouTube (search for the model you're interested in).

Most transceiver models and brands have an online community of active users. Such groups may be found on Facebook, Yahoo Groups, or Groups.io among other platforms. A Google search will help you locate a group for the radio you're interested in.

7) Buying a radio.

We're fortunate to have a number of good manufacturers and dealers serving the Amateur Radio community. Once you've made up your mind,

ARRL's online Club Search web page can help you locate clubs throughout the US.

visit your local dealer or contact one of the advertisers in *QST*. You'll have your new radio in no time.

Keep in mind that if you buy a good quality radio and you decide the radio is not a good fit for you, the used radio market will make it easy for you to sell it and recoup most of your money. However, if you buy a low quality radio you may have a harder time selling at the price you desire.

When selling a radio, it may be easiest to try at your local radio club or hamfest flea market. If you're willing to carefully pack your radio and ship it, then one of the online ham radio classified sites such as **swap.qth.com** or **www.eham.net/classifieds/** might appeal to you.

Next Steps

After a lot of careful research, you have picked a radio for portable use. First thing is to look over the manual that came with the radio. Keeping a copy of your radio manual/reference sheet both in electronic and paper format is useful to have on hand in the event you need to find out more about a radio feature or option. I also keep a copy of my charging times on the radio charger cable and a master reset card with my radio in case the need to reset my radio arises.

Don't forget to record the serial number and take a picture of the radio for insurance purposes. Keeping a copy of the receipt is also a good idea to have on hand. Consider signing up for the ARRL Insurance program (**www.arrlinsurance.com**), which not only covers equipment but also theft from unattended vehicles.

Accessories

What accessories should you consider purchasing to complete your kit?

The first items should be any data and power cables and/or adapters needed for your radio.

Next, when you are operating outside, environmental noise such as wind and other visitors if you are in a popular spot may make it difficult to pick out stations. Be sure to include a set of earbuds or headphones. Depending on how noisy the area is, noise canceling headphones might be a useful purchase. For hands-free voice operation, you might consider a headset with boom microphone.

If you plan to operate CW, you'll need paddles or perhaps a straight key. There are several good choices for small, light-weight paddles designed with portable operation in mind. Most modern radios

Headphones or earbuds can offer an advantage in hearing weak signals in noisy outdoor environments. Some operators prefer a headset such as this Heil unit with boom microphone for hands-free operation.

include a CW keyer with memories. If your radio does not, consider a battery-powered memory keyer for calling CQ and sending repetitive messages such as your location.

You will also need one or more antennas and rope or a support pole. We'll discuss those in detail in a later chapter. You'll also need coax and various RF connectors and adapters, some spare antenna wire for a quick emergency antenna, and flagging tape to mark guy wires or other hazards.

Most modern radios include a power and SWR meter of some type. That's important for portable operation where you are constantly installing, removing, and changing your antenna configuration. Consider a small SWR/power meter if your rig doesn't have one built-in. Going to the next step, an antenna analyzer will give you more information about what is going on with your antenna and will make it easier to adjust a multiband antenna that has to be re-tuned for band changes.

In humid conditions, or in a climate with large changes in temperature, it's a good idea to include desiccants to keep your gear dry in case of condensation. Operating outdoors, dust will accumulate so include a dust brush with your radio.

So how will you organize your radio and assorted gear? We covered that in detail in Chapter 3. A hard-sided crush-proof case with desiccant will be the safest way to transport your expensive items, but that type of case may be too bulky for truly portable use. Camera bags and other soft cases can be used to store your radio, but they are not as protective as a hard case.

If you plan to operate CW, you'll need a paddle. Palm Radio offers several small, lightweight paddles that are popular for portable operation.

Every portable antenna installation is different. If your antenna is not behaving as it should, an antenna analyzer such as this unit from RigExpert can be valuable in adjusting it for the desired frequency.

Chapter 5

Power Sources

Radios need power to run, and there are several considerations when evaluating power sources for your portable station. This LNR Mountain Topper transceiver carried to a SOTA summit by Zach, K1ZK, has low power requirements and a correspondingly small battery. (Courtesy Zach Manganello, K1ZK)

Unlike the home station with a virtually unlimited supply of power from the ac lines, every portable operation will be limited by its power usage and available power capacity. Whether running off batteries, solar power, or generators, power capacity available to the portable operator is the largest time constraint to a radio operation.

So how do you select the appropriate method for powering your radio? Power requirements should be based on:

- Your radio's preferred operating voltage
- Amp-hours consumed
- Type of power source
- Carrying weight
- Operating time

Power Requirements for Your Radio

The first consideration is what your radio requires for power — voltage and current. Specifications may be found in your instruction manual, and actual measurements are available from *QST* Product Reviews.

What Voltage Should You Use?

Radios, on average, prefer voltage input in the 13 to 14 V dc range. Typically they are designed for operation at 13.8 V dc, plus or minus 15%. That works out to a range of 11.7 to 15.9 V. Some low-power radios designed specifically for portable and battery operation, such as the Elecraft KX2 and KX3, the LNR Mountaintopper series, and the YouKits HB1B, are designed to operate with lower voltage. The ARRL Lab tests radios at the minimum specified operating voltage for *QST* Product Reviews.

When voltage starts to lag, radios may not work as effectively. Power output is often lower, and the lower voltage may even introduce spurious emissions. CW signals can start to chirp, and voice signals may become distorted.

Boost regulators, usually called "battery boosters," are available to raise a low voltage on a battery into a voltage range that the radio prefers. Boost regulators are essentially dc-to-dc switching power supplies that deliver a constant voltage output (say 13.8 V) over a range of input voltages. A word of caution: If you discharge your battery too far, you will likely damage it. Consult the specifications for your battery and set the minimum input voltage feature on the boost regulator to shut off, or at least warn you, when the minimum voltage is reached.

The opposite can also occur, when the available voltage may be

Table 1
Icom IC-7300, serial number 02001161

Manufacturer's Specifications	Measured in the ARRL Lab
Frequency coverage: Receive, 0.03 – 74 MHz; transmit, 160 – 6 meter amateur bands. Power requirement: Receive, 0.9 A (standby), 1.25 A (maximum audio); transmit, 21 A at maximum power output at 13.8 V dc ±15 %. Modes of operation: SSB, CW, AM, FM, RTTY.	Receive and transmit, as specified; (5.255 – 5.405 MHz, 60 meters). At 13.8 V dc: Receive, 1.05 A (maximum volume); transmit, 18.5 A (typical); 5 mA (power off). As specified.

Transmitter	Transmitter Dynamic Testing
Power output: 2 – 100 W; 1 – 25 W (AM).	HF, 0.7 – 104 W typical; 50 MHz, 0.5 – 97 W. 70 W typical at minimum specified dc voltage input.

Table 3
LNR Precision MTR-5B, serial number n/a

Manufacturer's Specifications	Measured in the ARRL Lab
Frequency coverage: 40-, 30-, 20-, 17-, and 15-meter amateur bands.	Receive and transmit, 7 – 7.15, 10.1 – 10.15, 14 – 14.15, 18.068 – 18.110, 21 – 21.15 MHz.
Power requirements: 6 to 12 V dc.	At 12 V dc: Receive, 19 mA; transmit 650 mA.
Modes of operation: CW.	As specified.

Transmitter	Transmitter Dynamic Testing
Power output: Up to 4.5 W.	At 12 V dc: 7 MHz, 5.2 W; 10.1 MHz, 5.3 W; 14 MHz, 5.0 W, 18.1 MHz, 4.7 W; 21 MHz, 4.7 W. At minimum operating voltage (6 V dc): 2 W typical.

QST Product Reviews report measured power requirements for transceivers under different operating conditions. In addition to current drawn by the transmitter and receiver at nominal rated voltage, power output at minimum rated voltage is also reported. The top measurements are for the full-featured Icom IC-7300 100 W transceiver. The bottom measurements are for the QRP, CW-only MTR5B Mountain Topper from LNR Precision, which is designed specifically for portable operation.

higher than the rated radio input voltage. In this case, a dc-to-dc converter may be used to bring a high voltage into the radio's required voltage range.

Because these devices are switching regulators, they can generate spurious signals and hash that will interfere with radio reception. Good ones include extensive filtering and are "radio quiet." Two boost regulators designed for ham radio use are available from:

• MFJ Enterprises: **www.mfjenterprises.com/Product. php?productid=MFJ-4416C**

• TG Electronics: **stores.tgelectronics.org/ the-new-n8xjk-boost-regulator/**

Battery boost regulators are designed to provide a constant nominal 13.8 V (adjustable) as battery voltage gradually decreases with use. The N8XJK boot regulator from TG Electronics (top) and MFJ-4416C incorporate extensive filtering to suppress RF interference from the switching regulator circuitry. To protect a battery from damage caused by excessive discharge, they can be adjusted to shut off when a minimum input voltage is reached.

One final word of caution: Some very inexpensive boost regulator modules are available online. These modules typically are not filtered to eliminate RF interference, and their output is not "clean" dc. The waveform has voltage spikes far above the nominal output voltage and can damage sensitive electronics. Buyer beware.

Amp-hours (Ah) Consumed

To determine your power usage, which will drive your power supply requirements, you first need to calculate how much power your radio will consume. A 10 W radio will have much lower power requirements than a 100 W station. Keep in mind if you have limited battery capacity, you can reduce your power output on a 100 W radio to conserve your battery.

This online calculator will help you determine what size battery (capacity in Ah) is required for a specific set of operating parameters, or how long you can expect a given battery to last. As with all calculators, you should enter data that is as accurate as possible for best results.

Recall that as a licensed operator, you should only use enough power to establish proper contact.

Power consumption while receiving can vary widely from radio to radio, and it can be higher than you might expect because of power-hungry displays, backlights, and audio amplifiers. *QST* Product Reviews typically show the current required under several different receive conditions. Radios designed for portable operation generally are designed for low current requirements for both receive and transmit.

While radio requirements are typically specified in volts and amps, batteries are typically specified in volts with capacity specified in ampere-hours (amp-hours, or Ah). An amp-hour is the amount of energy in a battery that will allow 1 A of current to flow for 1 hour. So a 10 Ah battery will deliver 1 A for 10 hours, or 2 A for 5 hours, or 10 A for 1 hour (assuming that it is rated to deliver 10 A — batteries have maximum current ratings too).

You can calculate your Ah needs using the calculator on the Four State QRP Group website (**www.4sqrp.com/Battery_Capacity/index. php**). That calculator is tailored for ham radio operation, and takes into account variables such as length of operation, receiver and transmitter current requirements, mode duty cycle, and operator duty cycle (how much time you will spend transmitting versus receiving).

Another consideration is any accessories that will also run from the same power source as your transceiver. That might include accessories such as a laptop computer, smartphone or tablet, external wattmeter, automatic antenna tuner, or lighting.

Operating Time

An important factor to consider is how much time you will operate. Are you just going out for a few hours, or will you be operating over several days? If it is an extended period, will you be in the field all the time, or will you be able to recharge batteries overnight?

If you are doing short 2 to 4 hour operating sessions, you can reduce the amount of battery capacity (Ah) needed and not worry about charging in the field. If your power needs are multi-day, then you will need larger batteries (higher Ah rating) and likely methods to keep those batteries charged appropriately. Access to recharging sources such as ac power mains, generators, or solar-powered charging systems might be required. Multi-day excursions will require more advance planning and careful considerations to ensure that your energy needs are met.

Once you have determined your power requirements, it's time to select an appropriate ac or dc power source.

AC Power Sources

Similar to the home station that uses commercial ac mains to power the radio system, portable operation sites occasionally will have ac power available. In these scenarios, be sure to pack a heavy duty extension cord, keeping in mind that voltage drops with distance. A power strip is another useful item to have with you, especially if you are powering multiple devices.

For portable events where commercial ac power is not present, generators can be used as a power source. Keep in mind that generator use at parks, campsites, and other public areas may be restricted or not allowed.

Inexpensive generators typically run at one speed — 3600 rpm (to produce 60 Hz) — and are noisy. Voltage and frequency regulation can be poor, varying with increased power demand. Today there is a lot of interest in a type of generator that is more fuel efficient, lighter weight and quieter — the inverter generator. Inverter generators produce high voltage, multiphase ac that is rectified to dc — similar to an automobile alternator. This dc power is then converted back to very clean and consistent ac power by a power inverter. A microprocessor controls the process as well as the speed of the engine.

The Honda EU2000i portable 2000 W inverter generator is very popular with portable operators.

Unlike older constant speed generators, inverter generators can run at idle, providing power to small devices. If demand for more power appears at the generator's outlet, engine speed increases. This feature is intended to improve fuel economy and can be switched on or off. Good quality inverter generators produce a well regulated voltage output with a clean sine wave, very close to the quality of power from commercial ac mains. Inverter generators can produce wideband noise and hash that interferes with nearby receivers. All gasoline generators can produce ignition noise from the spark plug.

A very popular generator with inverter that produces a clean sine wave and low levels of RF interference is the Honda EU2000i (**powerequipment.honda.com/generators/models/eu2000i**). This 2000 W generator weighs 46 pounds, is quiet, and is rated to run for up to 8 hours on 1 gallon of gas with a light load. Honda also offers 1000 W and 3000 W models. The EU1000i weighs 29 pounds, while the EU3000i weighs 78 pounds.

Generators do require maintenance, including oil changes and proper fuel storage due the increased ethanol content in fuel today. If you are storing fuel for an extended period, be sure to add a stabilizer such as PRI-G, StaBil, or Star Tron, available at your local auto parts store.

Along with maintenance, there are several cautions with running a generator. Gasoline engines produce carbon monoxide and must be run in well ventilated areas. Use an extension cord, and run all generators outside, far away from enclosed structures. Flag all extension cables so they are not a tripping hazard. Don't forget to bring along the manual for the generator for reference.

Battery Power

Battery, or dc power, is the preferred source for the portable operations due to its simplicity and availability. Currently there are two types of battery technologies commonly available:

1) *Sealed lead acid (SLA)*: Sealed lead acid batteries are very common in portable radio operations due to their low cost and wide availability. The downside is that they are heavy, bulky, and require proper care and maintenance.

SLA batteries come in a wide range of capacities, from 1 Ah to more than 100 Ah. They can be further divided into two types: starter and deep cycle. Starter batteries are what you would find in your vehicle. They are designed for a quick burst of high-current energy to start your engine. Conversely, deep cycle or "marine" batteries are better suited for radio use. They are designed to provide a constant flow of power over a long period of time. They can tolerate many deep discharge and recharge cycles without damage. Deep cycle batteries are best suited for powering radios in the field.

Lead-acid batteries contain a liquid acid that, if spilled, can be hazardous to both the operator and radio. Absorbed glass mat (AGM) batteries use a fine fiberglass mat that is saturated with battery acid and sandwiched between the plates. The plates and mats are tightly packed

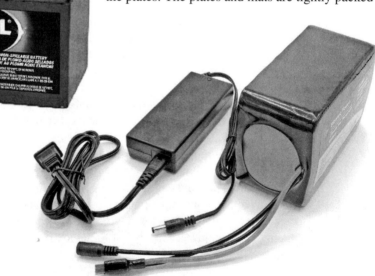

A typical deep-cycle SLA battery suitable for portable operation. These batteries are available from many sources in a wide range of Ah capacities.

The Bioenno Power BLF-1220A 20 Ah LiFePO$_4$ battery will power a 100 W transceiver for a couple of hours, yet weighs just 4.5 pounds. The battery is shown here with its matching charger.

inside the battery, so they are very resistant to shock and vibration and there is little or no liquid that could spill. SLA batteries are available with a gelled electrolyte as well.

2) *Lithium ion phosphate (LiFePO$_4$)*: LiFePO$_4$ battery technology is a relatively recent development and has starting gaining popularity in the amateur community. The main advantage to LiFePO$_4$ batteries is the weight-to-power ratio. LiFePO$_4$ batteries are significantly lighter in weight and smaller in size than SLA batteries with a comparable Ah rating. They can also be safely discharged more deeply than SLA batteries, and are rated for significantly more charge cycles than a typical SLA battery.

An example that is popular among portable operators is the 12 V, 20 Ah LiFePO$_4$ battery from Bioenno Power (**www.bioennopower.com**). The BLF-1220A weighs 4.5 pounds, about a ⅓ the weight of a comparable SLA battery. It has a maximum continuous discharge current of 40 A, much more than is needed for a typical 100 W transceiver. It will power a 100 W transceiver in a typical activation for several hours. The downside is that the LiFePO$_4$ technology is much higher in initial cost. As of early 2018, the BLF-1220A is around $200, while a Duracell 20 Ah deep cycle AGM battery is about ⅓ that price. The BLF-1220A is rated for 2000 or more charge cycles (compared to 300 to 500 for deep-cycle SLA batteries) so for frequent users the price difference is recouped over the long term.

Once you have purchased your battery don't forget to get the correct charger for your type of battery. If you have an SLA, then you should use a charger designed for that type of battery. Same goes for LiFePO$_4$ batteries. Using the incorrect charger can damage your battery or worse. Select the correct charger carefully.

Regardless of the battery you choose, the size and weight of the battery will be determined by how far you have to carry it. For quick outdoor operations located near your vehicle or home, weight is not so much an issue. Operations where all your gear is to be carried in by hand or on your back in a backpack will require smaller and lighter batteries.

Solar Power

Another dc power option is solar power. An important point is that in a portable operation, a solar panel will help augment your power use by charging a battery, but the panel will not provide the direct power for the radio. Typical portable solar panels do not provide enough power for a radio, and they produce higher voltage (17 to 20 V) than radios can use. Solar panels require charge controllers to bring the panel's voltage down

The Aspect Solar Energy Bar is typical of portable
power systems that use a lithium-ion battery to supply 12 V dc,
120 V ac at low current from an inverter, and several USB charging jacks.
A companion folding solar panel helps to keep the battery charged.

to a usable level and to manage proper battery charging. Examples
include:

- BuddiPole PowerMini: **www.buddipole.com/powermini.html**
- GENASUN MPPT Controllers: **genasun.com/products-store/
mppt-solar-charge-controllers/mppt-for-lithium-batteries/**
- Solar Battery Charge Controller by KI0BK:
ki0bk.no-ip.com/~pwrgate/LLPG/Site/Solar.html

Choose your solar charge controller carefully as the cheaper units
can produce RF interference and hash in your receiver. Higher quality
units are preferred. Be sure to test your system beforehand to determine if
this will be an issue.

Sizing solar panels is based on several factors, including cost, the
amount of power (watts) needed to charge the battery, availability of sunlight, and amount of time spent operating. For those operating for a long

The BuddiPole PowerMini charge controller manages battery charging from solar panels at currents up to 10 A. The display shows important battery and solar panel parameters.

period of time with plentiful sunlight, solar power can be a usable option. Those who operate for short periods of time, especially in the northern latitudes, may not find solar power worth the cost and setup time.

Sources of solar panels and technical information:

• Goal Zero Power Systems: **www.goalzero.com/**

• PowerFilm Solar Panels: **www.powerfilmsolar.com**

• Solar System Presentation by Jeremy, KF7IJZ: **youtu.be/8SuvAKZt0Vs**

Anderson Powerpoles and Accessories

If your radio, accessories, and battery don't have Anderson Powerpole connectors, you might consider adding them. Anderson Powerpoles are genderless, interchangeable power plugs that prevent you from connecting them with the incorrect polarity, a useful feature when connecting your battery in low light conditions. Powerpoles are very common in the emergency communications realm and have been widely adopted by amateurs everywhere.

These two Powerpole connectors are set up in the ARRL Amateur Radio Emergency Service configuration. The wide section on top is the hood and the narrow section on the bottom contains the clip that holds the connector. Shown installed are the 45 A connectors. [Steve Sant Andrea, AG1YK, photo]

This is the front of a Powerpole housing before the contact is inserted. The metal clip, which retains the contact in the housing, can be seen on the bottom. The hood above is where the contact will sit, once it is inserted. [Steve Sant Andrea, AG1YK, photo]

When installing Powerpoles, use the correct crimping tools. I use a crimper from Powerwerx that is perfect for the job (**powerwerx.com/tricrimp-powerpole-connector-crimping-tool**). Assembly instructions are available as well (**powerwerx.com/help/powerpole-assembly-instructions**). Anderson Powerpoles are so popular with hams that connectors, tools, and related parts are available from many sources.

Here are some suggestions when installing Anderson Powerpole connectors. When mating the red and black

This view shows a 30 A contact relative to the housing, oriented as it would be when it is installed. The round barrel at the left side of the connector is hollow and will accept #16 – 12 AWG size wires. The horizontal rectangular area on the left of the housing is the slot the dovetail slides into and the vertical slot is for the retaining pin. [Steve Sant Andrea, AG1YK, photo]

connectors, apply a little superglue on the inside mating surfaces for a permanent connection. You can also squeeze hot glue into the back of the connectors where the wires enter to give them some rigidity and protection. Finally, small cable ties can be used to temporarily join two connectors from two different items, preventing them from coming apart.

A useful accessory to carry with you is a Powerpole polarity checker for those times you may want to connect to a power source but are not sure of its polarity. See **www.w6trw.com/misc_documentation_articles/anderson_powerpole_tester/anderson_power_pole_tester.pdf**.

In some situations you may have one power source and multiple devices needing power. In this case, a Powerpole splitter should be used. They can range from a very simple power splitter block with several sets of Powerpole connectors, to a deluxe splitter with fusing and even USB jacks for charging cell phones and other gear.

In addition to power splitters, vendors offer a wide variety of Powerpole accessories. To make assembling your station easier, check out the available inline fuse holders, voltage and current meters, and short cables with Powerpoles on one end and a radio power connectors or terminals on the other.

This power splitter from QuickSilver Radio has six sets of Powerpole connectors for sharing power among multiple devices.

West Mountain Radio offers a line of RigRunner power distribution devices. This model can connect up to four devices using Powerpole connectors, with fuses on the input and each output. It also includes two USB jacks for charging mobile devices.

Some sources of Powerpoles, power splitters, tools, and accessories include:

- MFJ: **www.mfjenterprises.com**
- Powerwerx: **powerwerx.com**
- QuickSilver Radio: **www.qsradio.com**
- West Mountain Radio: **www.westmountainradio.com**

Many accessories, cables, and adapters are available for Anderson Powerpole systems, making assembly easy and flexible. This Bioenno 9 Ah LiFePO$_4$ battery comes standard with Powerpole connectors. The operator added an inline meter to monitor voltage, current, and Ah used, as well as an inline fuse holder and power cable that matches his transceiver.

For operations with high power requirements, a deep-discharge automotive battery can run one or more transceivers for an extended period. This unit from West Mountain Radio houses a standard Group 24 size deep cycle battery and incorporates a PWRgate power controller and RigRunner Powerpole distribution panel.

Connecting Your Power System

When connecting your power system, you need to take three important factors into consideration:

- wire size/length
- power consumed
- type of connectors

Size your power cables based on voltage drop, cable length, and maximum current carrying capacity of the wire. A chart for determining correct wire size and fusing requirements may be found at **assets.bluesea. com/files/resources/reference/20010.pdf**.

Undersizing a power cable will result in excessive voltage drop at the radio due to resistance in the wire and the possibility of overheating the wire itself because the current drawn exceeds the rating of the wire. The chart referenced above will help you select the appropriate two-conductor wire. Using stranded, tinned, insulated wire is the preferred choice because it is flexible and tolerant of vibration. Solid copper wire, while common, is stiff and not very a good wire to use in the field. Most radio manufacturers provide a power cable with their radios. Also, in their manuals they will indicate what size power cable you should use.

How do connect your power cables? Radios will vary from having dc barrel connectors to Molex and Anderson Powerpoles. As mentioned previously, Anderson Powerpoles are very popular and widely used because they are reliable and easily connected and disconnected. Standardizing your equipment power connectors and power source connectors will allow you to easily swap equipment and batteries in the field.

Chapter 6

Portable Antennas

Steve, WGØAT (foreground), and Steve, K7XC, enjoy hiking to remote SOTA summits. By necessity, the entire station, including antennas, is compact and lightweight. (Courtesy Steve Galchutt, WGØAT)

Antennas are one of the most important components of a portable station. While many operators focus primarily on the radio, an effective antenna system is essential for success with a portable radio station.

To compare, let's look at the home station antenna system. The antenna system is permanently installed and designed for maximum efficiency. There may be more than one antenna with more than one band capability. Antennas may be supported by a tower or pole, or hung high in a tree.

The portable antenna system, however, will always be a compromise in weight, efficiency, and convenience. It will always be a temporary installation, whether for a few hours or a few days. Limited time to set up and operate portable is often a consideration, and an operator may elect to install only one antenna. That antenna may limit the operation to just one band or a couple of bands.

Choosing a Portable Antenna

A little creativity goes a long way in setting up a temporary antenna support. Here a simple hiking pole jammed in some rocks holds up one end of a wire antenna.

So you bought your radio and you need to select an antenna. What is the best antenna? Unlike at the home station where you can select from various antennas that you have aloft, the best portable antenna is *the one you have with you*.

So how should you select an antenna for portable use? There are several different qualities you can use to select an antenna for your operating style and environment.

Weight

Similar to choosing radio equipment for portable operation, you need to look at the overall weight of your antenna. How will you transport your gear (including antenna) to your operating site? In a vehicle, and then 100 feet to a picnic table? Or in a backpack on a long hike to a summit? For some scenarios, weight will be a major issue while for others it may not. Fortunately most wire antenna systems weigh very little. On the other hand, if your antennas use masts and lots of aluminum tubing, weight will be a

At the other end of the spectrum is this fold-over tower mounted on a converted military deuce-and-a-half M109A3 truck that Pete, NØOY, uses in the field. (Courtesy Tanner Colvin, KDØIRW)

For backpacking, masts and antennas need to be broken down into small components.

factor if you have to transport them any distance.

Operating near a parked car will allow for a larger variety of antennas and more weight than someone backpacking. The less weight you can carry, the narrower your choices in the types of antenna materials available for your use. Those carrying a portable station by hand or in a pack will be limited mostly to wire antennas or other types of antennas that can be broken down into small components, usually under 3 feet (VHF or satellite antennas, for example). Anything larger becomes difficult to carry for any distance and will often get snagged by low-hanging branches or other obstacles.

Time

Another consideration in your antenna system is how much time you will have to set up and remove your temporary antenna. An event such as Field Day gives operators plenty of time to set up complex antenna systems, while those out for a day hike or picnic at the beach will have a very narrow window of time for antenna setup and removal. The more time you have, the more effort you can use in setting up your antenna system.

How You Will Use Your Antenna

Each portable operation may have different goals and criteria for operating, requiring antennas with different characteristics. Factors include:
- Operating frequency — one band or several?
- Mode — SSB operation usually requires a better signal than digital and CW modes
- Bandwidth — do you need to cover both the SSB and CW ends of the band?
- Transmit power — antennas with higher power ratings generally use larger and heavier components
- Efficiency — if you're running low power, you don't have power to waste

For example, if your time is limited, you may want to be equipped for several bands in case propagation is poor or activity is low on your first choice. Rather than setting up several monoband antennas for different bands, your time might be better spent setting up a multiband antenna and getting on the air more quickly. On the other hand, you might set up two different styles of antennas (such as a dipole and a vertical) to take advantage of their particular transmitting characteristics such as takeoff angle or directivity.

The mode you choose and bandwidth required can also influence what kind of antenna you select. For example, if you are using a digital mode such as PSK31, you might select a narrow bandwidth antenna because you will be on a fixed frequency most of the time. A magnetic loop such as the AlexLoop (**www.alexloop.com**) is a good example of this type of antenna. Magnetic loops have very narrow bandwidth and usually require retuning when you change frequency. Full-size dipoles, on the other hand, cover large segments of a band without retuning.

Another characteristic is how much power you plan to use. A low power station (QRP) versus a station running 100 W or more (QRO) can influence your selection based on the power limits of a particular antenna design. For example, most portable magnetic loop antennas are rated for 10 to 20 W.

Magnetic loop antennas have very narrow bandwidth and usually require retuning when you change frequency.

Efficiency refers to how well the antenna takes power from the radio and radiates it. Some antennas by their design will be more efficient than others. In general, small, compromise, or nonresonant antennas are not as efficient as full-size antennas. Some power is lost in loading coils or matching networks. If you are operating with low power, selecting antennas that are resonant may be a better choice versus those with loading coils.

Supporting Your Antenna

Most HF antennas need external support, whether it's a rope thrown over a convenient tree limb, a guyed mast, or a ground or vehicle mount. Exceptions include magnetic loops for HF and small Yagis for VHF/UHF that can be held by hand. However, these are in the minority and most portable antennas will need to be erected and supported somehow. It should be noted that some sites have very limited footprints for antennas or restrictions on using trees or driving stakes in the ground, and those locations can pose challenges to your ingenuity.

Methods for setting up your antenna will vary from site to site. The type of antenna you choose to use and the natural features and space available will determine how you get your antennas aloft.

If you're operating from your car, whether parked or in motion, the simplest solution is to use a mobile antenna. While mobile antennas work and have been used for countless successful activations, using a bigger antenna such as a dipole or vertical often gives better results. The bigger antenna will require some type of support.

Masts and Poles

The easiest method of supporting a mast is to attach your mast to your vehicle. There are several popular ways to do this.

Some people employ a metal base that they then drive over. The weight of

(Inset) If you are operating near a vehicle, you can drive onto a metal plate to anchor the base for a mast. (Courtesy Tim Carter, W3ATB]

Tanner, KDØIRW, uses a drive-on plate to support a substantial mast. (Courtesy Tanner Colvin, KDØIRW)

Johnny, K5ACL, uses a mount that slides into the trailer hitch on his truck. (Courtesy Johnny Twist, K5ACL)

With some ingenuity and rope or elastic cords, you can attach a lightweight mast to nearly any convenient object.

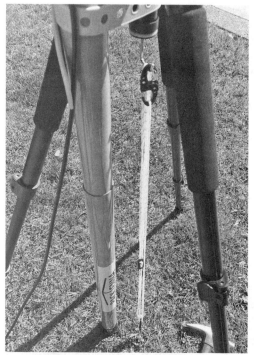

A camera tripod will support a lightweight mast if secured to the ground. (Courtesy George Zafiropoulos, KJ6VU)

the tire (and car) holds the antenna base plate securely. A short vertical pipe attached to the plate then secures the base of your antenna. A bracket of some type higher on the vehicle (attached to a luggage rack, for example) or rope guy lines can support the higher sections of the mast.

Another option is to use a trailer hitch receiver (if your vehicle has one) and fabricate a mount that fits in the receiver. A commercially made receiver-mounted bike rack or other accessory may also be suitable for an attachment point.

In a pinch you can even use a rear wheel and roof rack to keep a mast vertical. Set the base of the mast on the ground up against the wheel and tie it securely through the holes in the wheel. Also tie it to the roof rack for support higher up. On RVs, trucks, vans, and other high-sided vehicles, operators will sometimes install special mounting brackets for a quick mast attachment.

In the situation where no vehicle is present to use as an attachment point, look around for wooden or metal posts, parts of buildings, or trees that you can secure your antenna mast. If you're in a park or urban area, it's best to ask permission first, though.

The tree method may work in the eastern US where there are plenty of trees, but out west in areas of desert or other treeless areas, you will have to get creative. For example, you can use a tripod. A sturdy camera tripod, or a tripod designed to support lights or instruments, or even an

In a pinch, use a water bottle to hold the end of a wire antenna or guy rope.

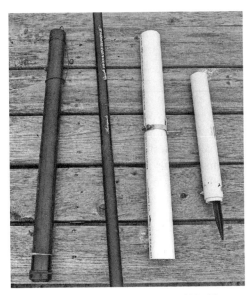
Collapsible masts are easily carried and ideal for supporting wire antennas.

Tent stakes and paracord are useful for guying masts and securing wire antennas.

improvised tripod will work. Be sure to stake down the tripod (if allowed), or use a bag of tools, sand, or even water secured to the center of the tripod as a counter weight.

Once your support or tripod is secure, you can attach a mast that will suspend your wire antenna elements. There are many different masts available that are made out of aluminum, fiberglass, or hard plastic. An important feature is the ability to collapse the mast for easy transport. Ultimately, you need to determine how much weight you will have aloft and plan your mast accordingly.

A cheap and readily available antenna that can be repurposed for antenna support is a collapsible fishing pole, usually around 20 feet in overall length. Another solution is a painter's pole, available in lengths up to 20 to 25 feet. Fiberglass poles that are part of a military tent system may also be used. These poles come in 4-foot sections and can support more weight than other masts.

Lightweight telescoping poles designed specifically for portable ham radio use are available from PackTenna (**packtenna.com**) and SOTABEAMS (**www.sotabeams. co.uk**). These masts are around 33 feet overall, a convenient number when using a 40 meter vertical element as it is the same length (33 feet). The SOTABEAMS Travel

Mast is just 26.5 inches when collapsed, very convenient for transport.

Some portable stations may even use the radio itself as the antenna mount. Backpack portable and lightweight antenna systems using vertical collapsible elements can use the antenna mount as the attachment.

For those areas where stakes are forbidden, rocks, weights, water bottles, or even gear bags can be used to hold guy and element lines where they need to be located. Be sure to flag your guy wires, stakes, tripod, antenna elements, radials, and coax if other people or animals are present. They might pose a tripping hazard. Ground radials especially can blend into the grass and be tripping hazards to pedestrians walking through the area. There would be nothing worse than someone passing through and getting caught up in your antenna system, bringing it crashing down while you are in the middle of a lively pileup.

If possible, rope off an area around your antenna at waist height to discourage people from getting tangled up in your antenna system. Ultimately it is your responsibility to make sure you are operating a safe portable radio station and that you don't create a hazard for others in the area. Unlike the home station, there are many more variables (people, pets, vehicles, and so forth) that may be out of your control.

Getting the Antenna Aloft

Weighted tennis balls or throw bags can be used to send a line over a branch.

Another option for setting up your antenna is to hang it aloft from trees or other elevated structures. While you might be able to climb a tree or structure yourself to get the line where you want it, that's not recommended because you increase your chances of injury by falling. Getting lines aloft from the ground is much preferred and safer.

As with antenna masts, there are several ways to get your antenna aloft while standing on the ground. The easiest method is to throw a line over a branch using what is available at the site. Rocks, your water bottle, even a large stick can be put into use.

If none of those items are

available, bringing your own throw weight with you might be necessary. I like to use old tennis balls filled with pennies or fishing weights. Tennis balls are easily obtained and a small loop can be fastened to allow for quick attachment. Adding a breakable line or rubber band between the loop and your throw line gives you a weak point in case the ball gets stuck in a tree. With enough force, that sacrificial line will break and drop your ball and line back to the ground.

A more expensive but common item in the arborist community is the throw bag. These bags are small nylon or vinyl sacks filled with lead shot and can weigh from 8 to 20 ounces. A common size is around 12 ounces. As with the tennis ball approach, adding a weak link between the throw bag and throw line might be worthwhile depending on how thick the trees are where you are attempting to get a line aloft.

The throw line should be a small diameter line with low friction. An example is ⅛ inch diameter polypropylene line, typically found in hardware stores. Another common throw line is small diameter nylon line often called mason's line or twisted nylon line. This line is around 18 gauge and is very inexpensive and easily obtained locally. Nylon line should be considered as a one-time-use, disposable item. Trying to coil it after use is inefficient as it tends to tangle very easily.

Another commonly used line is military paracord. While exceptionally strong, paracord has high friction when dragged across branches and can slow your throw bag or even prevent it from dropping back down.

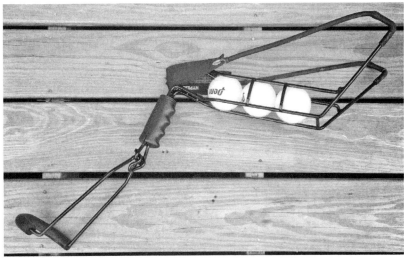

If throwing a line is difficult or won't get the antenna support rope high enough, consider a tennis ball launcher.

Strong, lightweight rope is needed for throw lines and antenna supports.

With these caveats in mind, paracord is also plentiful and inexpensive, making it another option to use as your throw line.

Finally, many amateurs use lightweight fishing line, often on a reel. It's commonly available, quite slippery, and can be purchased in high visibility colors so you can see where the line went. Fishing line is available in various weights; look for one with a high breaking strength.

When tossing the throw bag and line, you need to examine the ground around you. If you are in an area with lots of debris on the ground such as leaves, sand, snow, or grass, put down a blanket or Tyvek sheet and loosely lay out your throw line on the ground cloth. That will reduce snags or hangups of your line when throwing.

Before throwing your weight, verify that no one is near or in the area beyond your target. You don't want to hit anyone with your weight. Then simply throw the weight and line over the desired branch. Height achieved will be based on your throwing arm strength and the weight of the throw bag. Another option is a circular swinging technique. This requires practice to pull off successfully.

If throwing a line is difficult or won't get the antenna support rope high enough, another technique is employing a slingshot. Using a slingshot and small weight with a fishing line attached you can get you some decent height in a tree. A variation of a slingshot is a tennis ball launcher for dogs. Using tennis balls with line attached is another way to get lines aloft.

There are also techniques using powered devices. Pneumatic guns (aka "potato guns") have been used for years in the amateur community. These devices are made out of schedule 40 PVC pipe that's glued together. They use a combustible gas as a propellant to shoot a tennis ball or other projectile quite a distance. Extreme care must be taken in the construction and use of these devices. Misuse and poor craftsmanship may result in propellant burns or serious injury from plastic breaking apart. Also, the projectile itself can damage property or injure people. That said, if care is observed, pneumatic guns can launch your throw line to incredible heights not easily achieved with manual methods.

Another option is a crossbow or bow and arrow. Applying common sense and taking precaution so that nobody is on the receiving end of your arrow are important. Be aware that in some jurisdictions a slingshot, pneumatic gun, or bow and arrow may be illegal to possess and/or use. Verify your local laws concerning these devices before going out to your selected site. You're not exempt from the law just because you are using the device for an alternative purpose (hanging antennas) or don't know the rules.

Antenna Types

What types of antennas can you use for portable operations? You can use any antenna that you can carry, set up and that works with your radio. The antenna qualities listed near the beginning of this chapter should be used as a guide, but ultimately it is the operator's choice. It is fine to ask other operators what they are using and solicit suggestions, but after looking at options, select an antenna that meets *your* needs — after all you will be the one using it.

This section will present an overview of popular portable antenna types and some suggestions. There many more qualities of antennas that can be discussed, and many books have been written about them. If you are looking for ideas for portable radio antennas, check out the *ARRL's Portable Antenna Classics*, *ARRL's Wire Antenna Classics* (three volumes), or *ARRL's Vertical Antenna Classics*. The *ARRL Antenna Book* is another comprehensive resource. These titles are all available from the ARRL website (**www.arrl.org/shop**).

HF antennas commonly used for portable activations range from the most basic antennas such as the dipole to verticals, random wire/end feds, and magnetic loops. Some suppliers of antennas suitable for portable operation are shown in **Table 6.1**.

Table 6.1
Portable Antenna Sources

AlexLoop: **www.alexloop.com**	MFJ: **www.mfjenterprises.com**
Alpha Antennas: **alphaantenna.com**	MyAntennas: **myantennas.com**
Arrow Antennas: **www.arrowantennas.com**	Pacific Antenna: **www.qrpkits.com**
Buddipole: **www.buddipole.com**	PackTenna: **packtenna.com**
Chameleon Antenna: **www.chameleonantenna.com**	QRP Guys: **qrpguys.com**
Diamond Antenna: **www.diamondantenna.net**	SOTABEAMS: **www.sotabeams.co.uk**
LNR Precision: **www.lnrprecision.com**	Wolf River Coils: **wolfrivercoils.com**

Dipoles

A dipole fed with coaxial cable and supported by trees is probably the simplest and most effective antenna for portable operation. If trees are not an option, the antenna can be hung from a portable mast as an inverted V, with the dipole legs helping to guy the mast. The feed point is where the inverted V hangs from the mast, so the feed line is longer than with some other antenna types.

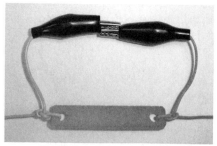

The SOTABEAMS link dipole is assembled in segments that are separated by insulators. Simply clip the segments together to extend the antenna length for covering a lower frequency band. (Courtesy Sean Kutzko, KX9X)

Dipoles can be made for a single band or for multiple bands. A dipole for 40 meters fed with coax will also work on 15 meters. Dipoles can be fed with ladder line (see the Feed Lines section below) and cover many bands with the help of an antenna tuner.

A popular multiband configuration is the "link dipole" which has several lengths of wire separated by insulators in each leg. Jumpers are connected between the segments to make the antenna electrically longer to cover different bands. For example, the antenna may cover 20 meters with no jumpers connected, 30 meters with the next segment added, and 40 meters with all segments connected.

Dipoles can also use loading coils or traps to cover multiple bands. Another popular multiband variation is the G5RV antenna.

An inverted V dipole on a collapsible mast is a simple and effective portable antenna. (Courtesy Sean Kutzko, KX9X)

The BuddiPole multiband dipole is popular among portable operators. (Courtesy Tim Watson, KB1HNZ)

Verticals

Vertical antennas can be made from aluminum tubing or wire, and they can cover one band or several bands. Verticals are popular because they require only one support and may or may not require guy ropes. Quarter-wave ($\frac{1}{4} \lambda$) verticals require four or more radials to work effectively, while half-wave ($\frac{1}{2} \lambda$) designs often require no radials. Another variation uses a $\frac{1}{4} \lambda$ vertical element and a single $\frac{1}{4} \lambda$ elevated radial, similar to a $\frac{1}{2} \lambda$ vertical dipole. The feed point is at the base of the vertical, so a short feed line will suffice.

Wolf River Coils offers loading coils for the base of a vertical antenna that can be adjusted for operation on several bands.

Vertical antennas require only one support at the base and can be adapted to a variety of situations.

If you are operating from a vehicle, one of the simplest and least expensive options is a hamstick mobile antenna on a magnetic mount.

If you are operating from or near a vehicle, a mobile HF antenna is another option. The simplest option is a helically wound whip (often called a "hamstick") on a magnet mount or lip mount. These antennas are made for a single band and are very inexpensive, but they are not particularly efficient antennas. A multiband motorized "screwdriver" mobile antenna is more efficient and covers a number of bands, but is considerably more expensive and more complicated to install.

End Fed Wires

Another popular option that requires just one support is an end-fed wire. The feed point is at one end and can be close to the radio with a short feed line. The two popular end-fed configurations are the random wire and the end-fed half-wave (EFHW).

The random wire is just that — a random length of wire fed at one end. Random wires can cover several bands with the help of the antenna tuner, although a good match will not always be possible. The end-fed half-wave is a half-wavelength long wire fed on one end. Some designs are fed with a 9:1 transformer and work on multiple bands.

Random wires and EFHW antennas work best with a counterpoise (a good ground or radial(s) laid on the ground).

The PackTenna random wire antenna takes up little space in a backpack and works on several bands with the help of an antenna tuner.

The end-fed half-wave (EFHW) antenna is a popular option. It covers multiple bands with a 9:1 transformer at the feed point.

Magnetic Loops

It's hard to beat the magnetic loop ("mag loop") antenna for locations with limited space or where compact, low-profile antennas are required. The typical portable magnetic loop antenna covers 40 through 10 meters, uses a 3 to 4 foot loop made from flexible coaxial cable, and

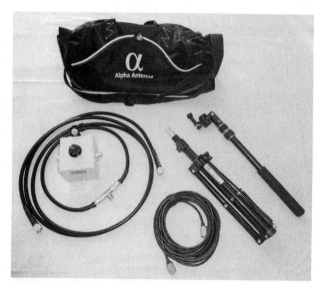

breaks down for transport in a small bag. A magnetic loop can be mounted on a small tripod, works well just a few feet off the ground, and is tolerant of nearby objects.

Typically the antenna has a tuning capacitor that must be adjusted carefully for operation on each band, and also when changing frequencies within a band. Tuning is very sharp, so some practice may be required.

Most portable mag loops are rated for low power (20 W or less).

This mag loop from Alpha Antennas is typical of portable designs that break down for easy transport, yet take just a few minutes to assemble.

Joe, N2CX, and Emily, KB3VVE, using W4OP mag loops at the Statue of Liberty. These antennas are ideal for low-profile operations. (Courtesy Joe Everhart, N2CX)

VHF/UHF Antennas

If you're planning to use a VHF/UHF handheld during your activation, consider bringing a better antenna than the stock flexible "rubber duck." For example, a telescoping whip that extends to full size for 2 meters or 70 cm has more gain than the stock antenna.

VHF/UHF antennas are small, so a directional antenna such as a 3- or 5-element Yagi is practical for 2 meters or 70 centimeters. Moxon beams are popular for 6 meters.

Arrow Antennas offers a line of VHF/UHF Yagis that break down for easy transport.

You can extend the range of a VHF/UHF handheld with a long aftermarket whip antenna.

The assembled Arrow Antenna for 2 meters and 70 cm, mounted on a tripod and ready for satellite or terrestrial contacts. It also can be handheld.

VHF/UHF antennas can be mounted on a light duty mast or tripod and rotated by hand. Some are even designed for handheld operation.

Amateur satellites can be accessed with low power and small antennas, offering portable operators a chance to try something different. Small handheld 2 meter/70 cm antennas for satellite operation are available.

Feed Lines

Along with the antenna, you need to consider what kind of feed line you will use. There are three types of feed lines: coaxial cable, ladder

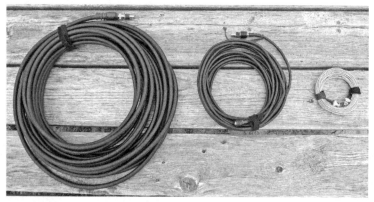

Coaxial cable is available in several sizes. The smaller cable is easiest to transport, but has the highest loss.

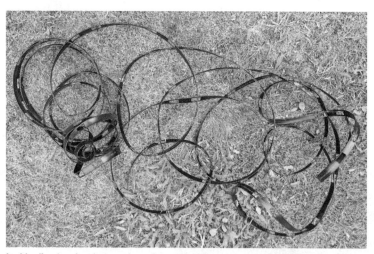

Ladder line has low loss and can be used with an antenna tuner to make a dipole that covers several bands. It's harder to transport than coax, however.

MFJ makes a line of loaded whip antennas designed for direct mounting on a low-power HF transceiver.

line, and direct attachment to the radio.

The first and most common feed line is coaxial cable. Most portable operators use small diameter cable such as RG-58, RG-8X, or other variations. Some operators use miniature cable such as RG-174 or RG-316 coax to save weight. However, high losses make miniature cable less attractive on the higher HF bands and unusable on VHF/UHF. **Table 6.2** shows the loss for 100 feet of various popular feed lines.

Select coax based on the overall length of your cable, the frequencies you will be operating on, and your power requirements. The longer the feed line, the higher the loss in dB, and the higher the loss of your transmitting power. I usually carry 25-foot lengths of RG-58 coax with a double female BNC adapter dummy corded to one end of each cable. That way I can easily join two 25-foot lengths together for that rare time when I need a longer coax run. You can explore the loss of various lengths and types of coax with a calculator at the Time Microwave website (**www.timesmicrowave.com/calculator/**).

If you operate portable often, you will find that your coaxial cables are a disposable item and you may need to replace them more frequently than at a home station. The act of coiling and uncoiling and using them outside in various climates will degrade their effectiveness over time. Do not hesitate to replace your feed lines as necessary.

Another feed line option is to use ladder line. Ladder line (parallel feed line) works well in keeping your power losses low. Large ladder line (450 ohm) used in home stations isn't very useful for portable stations due to its difficulty in winding up for storage, but 300 ohm TV-type twinlead

Table 6.2
Common Types of Coaxial Cable

Type	Impedance Ω	Loss per 100 feet (in dB) at 14 MHz	Loss per 100 feet (in dB) at 150 MHz
RG-8	50	0.7	2.5
RG-8X	50	1.3	4.5
RG-58	50	1.7	5.6
RG-174	50	3.1	10.3

is more portable-friendly. Large ladder line would be fine for Field Day and other long-term radio events where there is plenty of time to deal with it in a relaxed manner. A dipole fed with ladder line or twin lead can be used on multiple bands with low loss, but an appropriate antenna tuner is needed.

Direct attachment of the antenna to the radio is another option — think of VHF handhelds with their flexible antennas. This category includes HF antennas used in man-portable setups and antennas that use part of the element as the feed line which attaches directly to the radio itself. Direct attachment eliminates feed line loss and gives you one less item you have to carry for your operation. However, these antennas are a compromise and may not be very effective.

RF Connectors

One last feature of your antenna system is the type of RF connectors you will be using. Most desktop and mobile HF radios use the PL-259/SO-239 connectors, while some of the smaller portable rigs use BNC connectors. The RF connectors you use will depend on your radio. Many operators will standardize their RF connectors throughout their system for

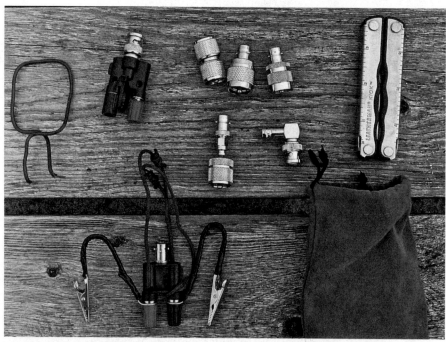

It's always a good idea to carry a variety of adapters for the coax connectors used in your setup.

A "dummy cord" made from a short length of paracord and some shrinkwrap tubing can help keep adapters from getting lost.

simplicity and uniformity. If you don't standardize on one connector type, you will need RF adapters. For example, you may use BNC connectors on all of your feed lines and antennas, and then use a BNC-to-PL-259 adapter at the radio. Regardless what connection system you choose, you should always have on hand RF adapters that allow you to switch between whatever types you have in your system.

A good addition to your gear is a set of covers that protect your RF connectors from becoming impacted with mud, water, and other environmental debris. SOTABEAMS offers dust covers that fit BNC and other connectors (**www.sotabeams.co.uk/ bnc-pl259-n-type-dust-cap-pack-of-4/**).

Another RF connector to add to your gear is the BNC-to-binding post adapter which allows you to connect the antenna elements directly to each post. This connection bypasses the coax feed line and gives you the ability to make and use random wire or improvised antennas as needed. Another advantage is that if your coax connector fails, you can cut off the failed connector and strip back the coax shield and center conductor to connect the coax to the banana posts.

Antenna Accessories

You have your antenna and feed line — what kind of accessories should you include?

Antenna Tuner

If you are using non-resonant antennas and your radio does not have an internal antenna tuner, an antenna tuner should be added to your list.

A small antenna tuner, such as this Emtech ZM-2, can help when your radio's internal tuner can't find a match.

Internal antenna tuners built into radios often have limited tuning ranges, so it's a good idea to check your radio and antenna on all the frequencies you plan to use before heading out. If your radio's internal tuner can't find a match, consider an external tuner — they often have a greater range.

Here are some sources for manual and automatic antenna tuners for a variety of power levels and portable/mobile antenna types:

- Emtech: **steadynet.com/emtech/**
- LDG Electronics: **www.ldgelectronics.com**
- MFJ Enterprises: **www.mfjenterprises.com**
- Pacific Antenna: **www.qrpkits.com/sota.html**
- QRP Guys: **qrpguys.apps-1and1.com/ end-fed-half-wave-sota-antenna-tuner**
- SOTABEAMS: **www.sotabeams.co.uk**

Spare Parts

Carrying spare antenna wire to improvise antennas is good idea. I always carry an emergency antenna in my radio bag that consists of a BNC-to-binding post RF adapter, along with #26 magnet wire to use as a random wire antenna. This wire is fragile, but it doesn't take much space and makes a good one-time-use antenna. If I have no other antennas with me, or my main antenna fails, it can keep me on the air.

Other items might include spare guy wire and ground stakes, paracord or twine, and RF adapters.

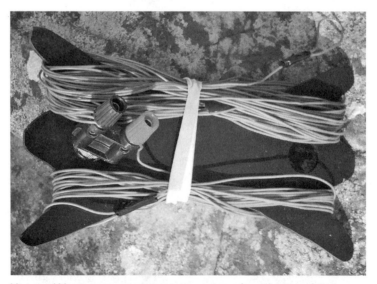

It's a good idea to carry a spare emergency antenna in case you run into problems with your primary antenna. A BNC-to-binding post adapter and some small wire can be used to make a quick random wire antenna.

Antenna Analyzer

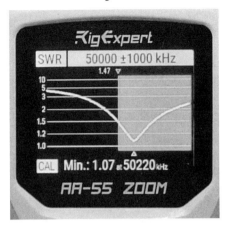

An antenna analyzer is very useful for tuning multiband antennas or diagnosing problems.

Most modern radios have a wattmeter and/or SWR meter built-in. Depending on the type of antenna, carrying a SWR analyzer might be necessary. Antenna analyzers make it easier to change bands with a multiband antenna, or to diagnose a problem with an antenna that is not working properly in the present location. For simple antennas already set up for your radio, you may not need to carry one.

Chapter 7

Propagation and Spotting

Online resources abound for checking current propagation and spotting your activation so chasers can find you.

When band conditions are good, there are endless opportunities for contacts. When conditions are poor, every contact is a struggle. That's especially true for portable operations where you may be using low power or less-than-optimum antennas. Also, when your signal is weak you may have trouble getting the attention of other operators on the band. You can increase your chances of success by learning more about propagation and by using various spotting methods to let chasers know to look for you.

Propagation

Propagation is a subject frequently discussed among amateurs because of its large influence on operators making successful contacts. For the portable operator, you have two options in dealing with propagation.

First, you can set up and get on the air regardless of the solar conditions and start calling CQ. Depending on the time of day/week, propagation on the band(s) you choose, and antenna setup, you may or may not have success with this method.

The second method is to look at the look at the current propagation forecast and future predictions. Working portable, the amount of time you have available may be limited, so any techniques that can increase your chances of making contacts will make your operation more successful. Here are some resources for finding current propagation conditions and forecasts, and learning more about propagation.

• Real Time DX HF Propagation Prediction Above 5 MHz (ON4AA): **hamwaves.com/propagation.prediction/en/index.html.**

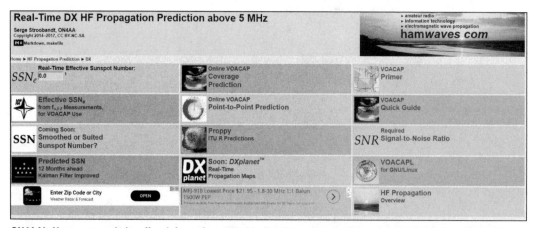

ON4AA's Hamwaves website offers information and tools for HF propagation. The online VOACAP application gives point-to-point propagation predictions based on current solar conditions and station equipment (antenna, power level) at each end of the path.

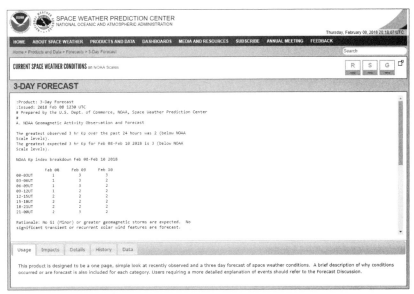

A three-day propagation forecast is just one of many resources available at NOAA's Space Weather Prediction Center.

- NØHBH Propagation Tools and Solar Data:
www.hamqsl.com/solar3.html
- NOAA Space Weather Prediction Center:
www.swpc.noaa.gov/communities/radio-communications
- Space Weather Woman: **www.spaceweatherwoman.com**
- The Watchers: **watchers.news/category/geomagnetic-storms/**

Real-Time Propagation Data

While propagation forecasts are helpful, getting real-time data is the most accurate way to determine current conditions. Once you leave home, getting up-to-date propagation information will depend on what equipment and connectivity you have available.

For current conditions, you can use your HF radio to listen to automated beacons to see what paths to various parts of the world are open. These beacons are sponsored and maintained by the Northern California DX Foundation (NCDXF)/International Amateur Radio Union (IARU) International Beacon Project. A helpful operating aid is to add the beacon frequencies for the bands you operate into the memories of your radio. By doing so, you can quickly scan through the different bands to see which are open and which are closed.

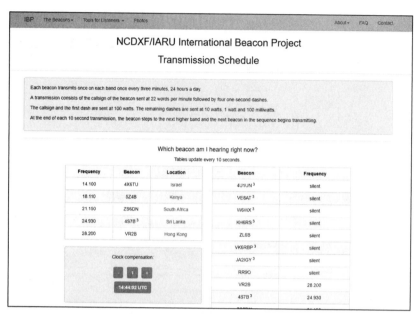

NCDXF/IARU International Beacon Project

Transmission Schedule

Each beacon transmits once on each band once every three minutes, 24 hours a day.

A transmission consists of the callsign of the beacon sent at 22 words per minute followed by four one-second dashes.

The callsign and the first dash sent at 100 watts. The remaining dashes are sent at 10 watts, 1 watt and 100 milliwatts.

At the end of each 10 second transmission, the beacon steps to the next higher band and the next beacon in the sequence begins transmitting.

Which beacon am I hearing right now?

Tables update every 10 seconds.

Frequency	Beacon	Location		Beacon	Frequency
14.100	4X6TU	Israel		4U1UN [3]	silent
18.110	5Z4B	Kenya		VE8AT [3]	silent
21.150	ZS6DN	South Africa		W6WX [3]	silent
24.930	4S7B [3]	Sri Lanka		KH6RS [3]	silent
28.200	VR2B	Hong Kong		ZL6B	silent
				VK6RBP [3]	silent
				JA2IGY [3]	silent
				RR9O	silent
				VR2B	28.200
				4S7B [3]	24.930

Clock compensation:

14:44:02 UTC

Beacons such as those sponsored by the NCDXF/IARU International Beacon Project can help you assess current conditions to different spots on the globe.

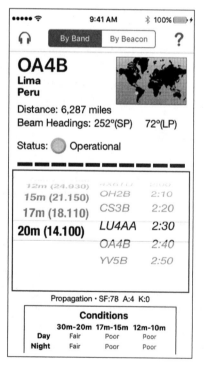

The BeaconAid app offers information for identifying and using the NCDXF/IARU beacons.

There are also a number of independent beacons on 10 meters and the VHF/UHF bands. These are particularly useful for spotting band openings when not many stations are active.

Here are some resources for using beacons:

• NCDXF/IARU International Beacon Project: **www.ncdxf.org/ beacon/beaconschedule.html**

• BeaconAid-HF App: **itunes. apple.com/us/app/beaconaid-hf/ id307460004?mt=8**

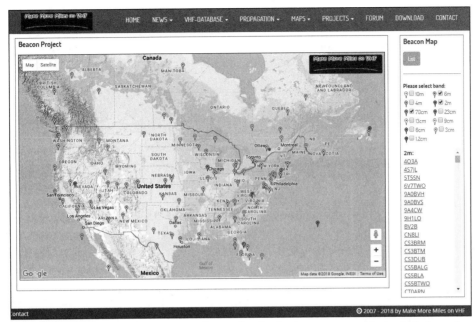

Make More Miles on VHF is a map-based online service showing beacons around the world that operate on 10 meters through microwaves. Here, 6 and 2 meter beacons in the U.S. are shown.

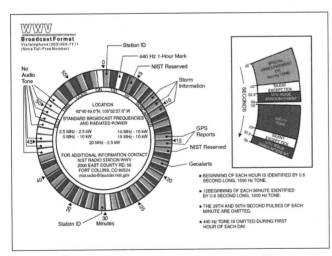

You may be familiar with the time "ticks" from WWV and WWVH, but they also broadcast current solar terrestrial conditions every hour. No internet needed — tune your HF radio to a WWV frequency and listen at 18 minutes past the hour (45 minutes past for WWVH).

• NCDXF Beacon App:
play.google.com/store/apps/details?id=com.wolphi.clock&hl=en

• Make More Miles on VHF (VHF Beacon Map):
www.mmonvhf.de/bcn_map.php

Along with automated beacons, you can tune into the WWV/WWVH broadcasts. In addition to acting as a time and frequency standard, these stations broadcast solar terrestrial information once an hour. WWV transmits solar data including A and K index or geomagnetic storm warnings at 18 minutes after the hour, and WWVH transmits this information at

45 minutes after the hour. (Generally an A index at or below 15 or a K index at or below 3 is best for HF propagation.) WWV is located in Fort Collins, Colorado, and broadcasts on 2.5, 5, 10, 15, and 20 MHz. WWVH in Hawaii is on 2.5, 5, 10, and 15 MHz. Both transmit in AM mode.

For more information, see:
- Band Conditions: **www.bandconditions.com**
- National Institute of Standards and Technology (NIST): **www.nist. gov/pml/time-and-frequency-division/radio-stations**
- NOAA Space Weather Prediction Center: **www.swpc.noaa.gov/ products-and-dat**a
- What the Numbers Mean: **www.arrl.org/ the-sun-the-earth-the-ionosphere**
- RF Propagation Analytics: **dxdisplay.caps.ua.edu**

Internet-Based Signal Reports

In recent years, amateurs have developed several resources that allow you to transmit a signal and quickly receive signal reports from a network of automated receivers via the internet. These reports let you know how well you are being heard in various locations at that moment.

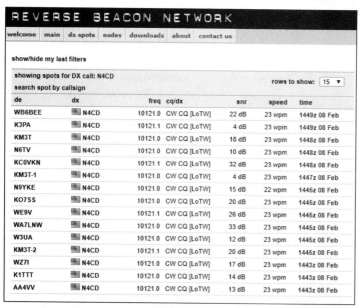

For CW operators, a useful method to check real-time propagation is to use the Reverse Beacon Network (RBN). Using CW, call CQ a few times followed by your call sign a few times. CW "skimmers" (wideband receivers with special software) stationed throughout the world listen for CW traffic on all bands, decode it, and post call signs heard and signal levels to the internet for viewing. These reports will tell you where your signal is being received and give you an idea of which paths

The Reverse Beacon Network (RBN) is a network of wideband "skimmer" SDR receivers that monitor large portions of the amateur bands and report CW and RTTY stations heard (call sign, frequency, and signal strength) on the RBN website in near real time. It's a great tool for portable operators to see how well they are getting out to various areas around the world. It's also a great tool for chasers to use to find activators.

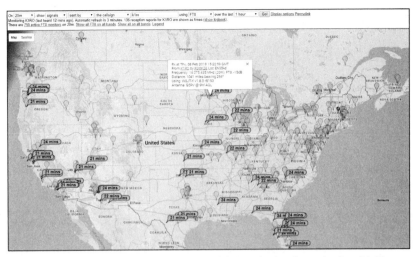

PSKreporter is a map-based website showing digital mode signals received worldwide in near real time. Users can select a call sign of interest, mode (PSK31, FT8, JT65, CW, RTTY and many more) as well as a band (or all bands). The map shows which stations have received the target station, as well as how recently (for example, a flag with "24 mins" means reception at that location 24 minutes ago). Click on a flag for call sign, frequency, mode, received signal strength, and other details.

are best based on received signal levels. Reception reports are available at **www.reversebeacon.net** (search for your call sign, or the call sign of interest). Note that the skimmers listen in the CW portion of the bands, so sending in the SSB portions may not be received.

Don't do CW? If you have digital capability, you can use PSK31 or other digital modes to call CQ and use PSKreporter (**pskreporter.info**) to find out where your signal is reaching. Note that PSKreporter shows signals heard on PSK31, CW, RTTY, JT65, and FT8 among other modes.

WSPR or Weak Signal Propagation Reporter (**wsprnet.org/drupal/**) is a one-way digital mode that also can be used to determine current propagation conditions. SOTABEAMS (**www.sotabeams.co.uk**) makes a device called WSPRlite that works with the DXplorer website (**www.dxplorer.net**) for testing propagation and antennas using WSPR.

If you have access to the internet, there are various DX clusters such as DXsummit (**www.dxsummit.fi**) that show call signs heard or worked by other stations. Those reports can give you an insight into what regions of the country and world are currently completing contacts. DX clusters and other spotting sites are discussed in detail in the next section.

Current propagation information isn't limited to just HF. VHF propagation maps also exist for those operating 50 MHz and above.

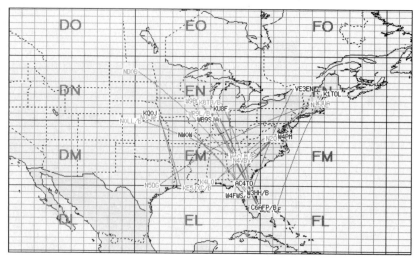

The DX Maps site shows reported QSOs in a graphical form, with the path indicated by a line with call signs at each end. This map shows a 6 meter E-skip opening in progress.

- DX Maps: **www.dxmaps.com**
- VHF propagation maps: **aprs.mountainlake.k12.mn.us**
- Worldwide Tropospheric Ducting Forecast: **www.dxinfocentre. com/tropo_wam.html**

Another trick to see if you are being heard in different parts of the country is to listen to WebSDR (**www.websdr.org**), an online radio service that allows you to listen to your operating frequency from different regions. By calling CQ on your radio and listening on the various WebSDR online receivers, you can verify where you are reaching.

Over the course of your operating, it can be helpful to keep a record of the propagation conditions on the days you are on the air. Recording not only the propagation data but also plotting out your contacts on a map (**www.qsomap.org**) gives you an idea of propagation trends over time.

To learn more about the science of propagation, check out the ARRL's propagation web page (**www.arrl.org/propagation**) and *Propagation and Radio Science* by Eric Nichols, KL7AJ, published by ARRL (**www.arrl.org/shop/**).

Spotting

You have arrived at your operating site, your antenna is set up and your radio is tuned and ready to go, so how do you increase your chances of making contacts? Spotting is an internet-based operating aid that helps those looking to make contacts with stations fitting specific criteria such

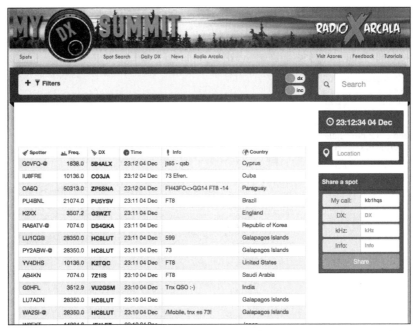

DX Summit is perhaps the best known DX spotting site. Spots include call sign worked, call sign of the spotter, frequency, time, and a free-form Info field (often used for mode, special location designator, and so on).

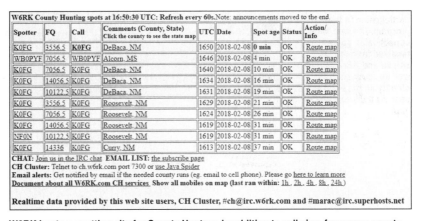

W6RK hosts a spotting site for County Hunters. In addition to call sign, frequency, county, and time, the site also links to route maps so chasers can see what's coming up.

In addition to real-time spots for SOTA activations, the SOTAwatch website has an Alerts feature showing upcoming activation information. In addition to call sign and date/time, activators can upload details such as band/frequency/mode and other information of interest to chasers.

SOTAwatch2

Home | Spots | Alerts | Reflector | Website | Summits | Recent Summit Info | Database
Video | Photos | Shop | Mapping | Facebook
This page refreshes every 5 minutes. Last updated 16:55:38 UTC.

Upcoming Activations

Thursday 8th February 2018

11:00	DL8MEK/P on DL/CG-065		145.500-fm
	+-30 min (Posted by DL8MEK)		
11:30	M0OAT on G/DL-035		5.2605-cw,10-cw
	Also other bands and modes (Posted by M0OAT)		
12:15	HB9TWM/P on HB/SG-037		7.032-cw
	(Posted by HB9TWM)		
14:15	F/HB9CBR/P on FL/VO-154		7-18cw
	together with F/HB9BIN/P (Posted by HB9CBR)		
14:15	OK/OM2JU/P on OK/LI-010		7.032-cw
	Freezing (Posted by OM2JU)		
15:00	DL/HB9BQU/P on DM/BW-110		10-cw,7-cw,14-cw
	(Posted by HB9BQU)		
15:45	NA6MG on W6/SD-335		5->18cw
	S+6, might activate SD-501 too if time permits (Posted by NA6MG)		
17:30	AA0BV on W6/NS-290		7.033-cw
	also 146.52 fm (Posted by AA0BV)		
18:00	K9PM/P on W7A/YU-148		5.332-cw
	60-17 mtr cw starting on 60 (Posted by K9PM)		
18:00	NS7P on W7O/WV-076		14.062-cw,10.112-cw,7.032-cw
	(Posted by NS7P)		
19:00	AE9Q on W7A/AE-051		7.195-ssb,14.347-ssb
	Time +/-; YL is with me, so quick SSB activation only (Posted by AE9Q)		
19:00	WG0AT on W0C/SP-074	7.032-10.112-14.062-18.092cw,146.52-fm	
	K7PX on 30m + SP-113(?) http://aprs.fi/wg0at-7 or K7PX-7 (Posted by WG0AT)		
19:30	KX0R on W0C/FR-170	7.033-cw,10.113-cw,14.063-cw,18.093-cw	
	ETA approx - looking for S2S - bands may vary (Posted by KX0R)		

Reflector Latest

SOTA News February 2018
by G0VOF, #3 by G0VOF, 44hrs ago

Change of callsign (on Reflecto
by K3ISI, #31 by WX7EMT, 66mins ago

Yaesu FT-818
by YO9IRF, #2 by DD5LP, 77mins ago

[POLL] Chaser DX antenna typ
by EA2IF, #2 by G6PJZ, 78mins ago

VK JA ZL - EU S2S 10 March 20
by VK1AD, #18 by DD5LP, 2hrs ago

This Friday the 9th of Feb G/W
by M0SER, #5 by M0SER, 3hrs ago

100th unique
by G6PJZ, #5 by G0RQL, 3hrs ago

Sota Fun Evenings
by M1EYP, #80 by M1EYP, 4hrs ago

Chasing non-SOTA operator on
by K6WRU, #12 by K0NR, 12hrs ago

Hitting the Wall, a Death Valley
by W6PNG, 12hrs ago

Spring W4 SOTA Campout April
by KI4SVM, #38 by KI4SVM, 18hrs ago

Long term pre-planning?
by SP9MA, #10 by AB3TQ, 18hrs ago

W2/GA (Adirondack) SOTA Part
by N3TWM, #28 by MOVED, 18hrs ago

>> more topics...

WWFF hosts a WWFFwatch DX-cluster page with real-time spots for stations participating in that program. The web page consolidates spots received from the DX cluster and RBN, as well as spots entered directly on the page or sent via the smartWWFF app.

as DX countries, US states, certain call signs, or specific amateur activities. When you are spotted, you can greatly increase your odds of making contacts.

Spotting information is entered into a form on one of the online DX clusters, and then it propagates online for others to view in near real time. A spot consists of a call sign, frequency, and activity information. For example: KB1HQS 14062 SOTA W1/AM-001 (KB1HQS is on 14.062 MHz from Mt Washington in New Hampshire, SOTA summit W1/AM-001). If you can't find someone to spot you, you can spot yourself ("self-spotting"). Here are some of the more popular general spotting websites:

- DXheat: **dxheat.com/dxc/**
- DXsummit: **www.dxsummit.fi**
- DXscape: **www.dxscape.com**
- DX Watch: **www.dxwatch.com**
- HamSpots: **hamspots.net**
- RF Propagation Analytics: **dxdisplay.caps.ua.edu**

While spotting is primarily designed for announcing DX contacts, it can be a useful tool for stateside contacts when doing specific radio activities. Examples include special events, rare grids or states, unusual propagation conditions, domestic contests, or unique operating events that other operators may be interested in.

Some activities have their own dedicated spotting sites that are specific to that activity. Here are some examples:

- ARLHS BeaconBot: **arlhs.com/beacon-bot/**
- SOTAwatch: **www.sotawatch.org**
- W6RK County Hunter's page: **ch.w6rk.com**
- WWFFwatch: **wwff.co/dx-cluster/**

Some activity-specific sites offer the opportunity to pre-register an activation as a reminder to other operators of your upcoming event. This is especially useful if you can't send a spot in real-time during your activation.

While there are many computer programs that will alert you to band openings and other criteria you select, in the field it is not always possible to bring a laptop or have an internet connection. A solution is to bring a cell phone with an app such as HamAlert (**hamspots.net**). This application allows the user to set up filters using specific criteria, and then the app can alert the user of filtered requests via text, e-mail, or the app itself. Creating a filter to alert you when your call sign is spotted gives you verification that you have been spotted. See my website (**kb1hqs.com**) or YouTube channel for a video review of HamAlert.

Accessing Spotting Sites in the Field

So if you are away from home, how do you access the spotting sites? First, you need to determine what tools you will have available to access the cluster. Your options may include a cell phone with texting or internet capability, commercial satellite access (Iridium/Globalstar), and any amateur transceivers that you have with you.

There are four ways to spot yourself while portable. Unlike the radio shack at home where internet is readily available, being out in the field requires different techniques and equipment.

Internet

If you are operating in an area with free Wi-Fi available and you have a smart phone/tablet or laptop, accessing Wi-Fi will allow you to use the standard internet functionality that you would have at home. Your home cable provider such as Comcast or AT&T may also provide access to various hotspots located throughout the US to you as a paid subscriber of their service. One example is Comcast (**wifi.xfinity.com/faq.php#find-a-hotspot**).

HamAlert allows the user to set up filters using specific criteria, and then the app can alert the user of filtered requests via text, e-mail, or the app itself.

Cellular Phone/Data

If local Wi-Fi isn't available, accessing the internet via your cell phone using cellular data is your next option. This discussion assumes that Wi-Fi is not available and the user is relying solely on cellular data.

Cell phones today have the capability of texting (SMS), phone, e-mail, and web browsing. Unlike web browsing or making voice phone calls, texting uses very little bandwidth and often works in areas with limited cellular connectivity. There are several options to spot using texts:

1) You can text a friend or family member to spot you. Make a list with names and numbers prior to your trip. If a person on the list is not familiar with spotting contacts, sit down with them beforehand to demonstrate how to post a spot. Giving them a script to use with the caveat they need to modify the frequency and time for your current operating activities can be helpful.

2) Text (SMS) to your Twitter and Facebook accounts. Like everything else in our society, Amateur Radio can be found on online social media sites. Many operators have personal pages with posts about their recent contacts, pictures of their shacks, and other amateur related information. These sites can be used with texting to post status updates and spots.

For instructions on setting up and using Facebook text, see **www.facebook.com/help/170960386370271?helpref=faq_content**. For Twitter texts, see **support.twitter.com/articles/14014**. When you've set up Facebook texts, you can send a text (SMS) to 32665 (FBOOK) to update your status and get notifications without using data. For SMS to Twitter, use 40404.

While operating in the backcountry with little to no cell service, I often find that the Facebook app opens and functions even when texting and web browsing does not. If you find yourself in this situation, you can use that to your advantage by posting a request for a spot on various Facebook ham radio groups.

Another trick when there appears to be very limited connection is to turn your phone to airplane mode on and then off so it will re-establish itself with the local cellular tower. Often it will give you a brief window of decent connectivity allowing you to spot and make social media posts before dropping out again.

3) Hotspot using an external device and phone. If you need to use a laptop in the field and lack Wi-Fi for internet connectivity, you may be able to tether your phone to your laptop so that the cell phone data is used by the laptop as if you were on the internet at home. Speeds may be slower depending on your cell data plan and signal strength.

Another option is to use a dedicated hot spot device that uses cellular connectivity to provide a Wi-Fi signal with internet access. There are many different manufacturers and models. Each device will require the user to purchase a prepaid cell plan (SIM card). One of the more important features on some models is the ability to attach an external antenna, a useful feature when in remote rural areas with poor cellular coverage. Hotspots can also be used to create mobile APRS iGates and digital hotspots such as the SharkRF openSPOT.

With a cellular or Wi-Fi connection, there are a multitude of ham radio apps and web pages that can be extremely useful for portable use. Examples for iOS devices include HamAlert and WW1X's SOTA GOAT. Android users have apps such as HamAlert and SOTA Spotter.

What about websites that don't offer an app? A shortcut to save time is to create an "add to home screen" function that allows you to create a virtual app on your cell phone for quick access to the website. This way all of your important websites are saved on your phone without you having to type them into the browser each time you want to use them.

Radio RF

What if you do not have your cell phone or laptop with you, or you are in an area with no service? You can use your radios to assist you with spotting. The easiest way to ask the person you are in a conversation with to spot you. This can bring limited success depending on how familiar the other person is with spotting. Locally, you can use a VHF repeater to see if anyone can assist you.

Another method is to utilize the APRS network and send text (SMS) or e-mail to your spotting group list. With the ability to text, you can utilize the texting methods listed previously for spotting to social media sites. Here are some resources:

- APRS to SMS: **smsgte.wixsite.com/smsgte**
- APRS2SOTA: **www.sotaspots.co.uk**

How can you verify that your APRS to SMS message is getting out? You can set up a free app called Stringify (**www.stringify.com**) to alert you when your call sign has been received as a transmitted APRS signal.

Another digital technique to get an e-mail out is to use Winlink

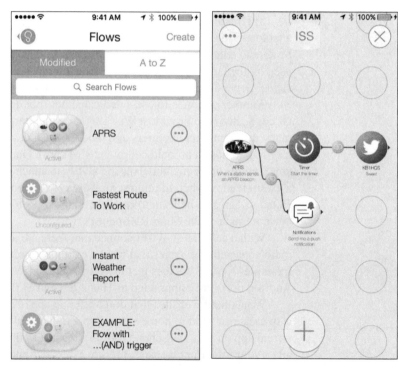

You can set up a free app called Stringify (www.stringify.com) to alert you when your call sign has been received as a transmitted APRS signal.

(**www.winlink.org**) for sending e-mail over HF radio. PiGate (**www.pigate.net**) is another system that can be used to send e-mail through Winlink via HF radio or VHF packet radio.

Commercial Satellite Access

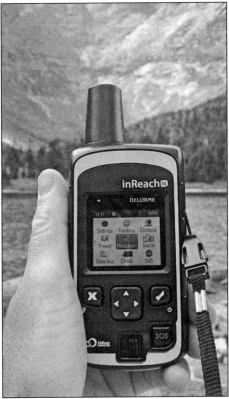

Stuart, KB1HQS, keeps in touch from remote areas using his DeLorme InReach two-way satellite communication device. (Courtesy Stuart Thomas, KB1HQS)

InReach (**explore.garmin.com/en-US/inreach**) is a fairly recent two-way satellite communication device. It was designed for those in remote areas that lack cellular coverage. The InReach system uses the Iridium satellite network and allows the user to request emergency help if needed. It also provides for texting or e-mailing friends and family with status updates or other relevant information. Posting on social media such as Facebook and Twitter is also possible with InReach.

The downside of this service is the cost of the hardware and monthly access fees. While InReach service many not be needed by many portable operators, for those offshore or in remote backcountry areas, it may be a useful tool to be used during an emergency as well as spotting for ham radio.

Summary

To maximize your time at your operating site and to make a lot of contacts, you can study the propagation and choose the appropriate bands and best times to get on the air. Using the various spotting techniques can help increase the awareness of your on-the-air operation and increase your contacts as well.

Chapter 8

On the Air Activities

Emily, KB3VVE, building her activator totals from a park. (Tim Carter, W3ATB, photo)

Once you have assembled and tested your portable station and stepped out of your ham shack, what can you do? While you may be content to just set up your portable station and make a few contacts, portable and mobile stations can participate in a wide range of organized operating activities. Some of these activities offer participation on an ongoing basis, while others are held at specific times (usually on weekends) to encourage as many stations as possible to be on the air at the same time.

Awards Programs

A number of organizations sponsor ongoing awards programs for portable or mobile operators. In general, these programs feature "activators" who do "activations" by operating from a specific type of location. Examples include summits, lighthouses, islands, and parks. Each location has a unique identifier of some sort, and the sponsors publish a list of qualifying locations and identifiers. Activators are hunted by "chasers" — stations trying to collect contacts with as many of the unique identifiers as they can. Although most chasers are operating from home stations, if two activators are on the air at the same time, they will often try to work each other. Awards programs run continuously, although some offer annual awards as well as lifetime awards. Activations occur every day, although activity is often higher on weekends.

Sponsors offer awards at various levels for both activators and chasers. For activators, the award is typically for activating a minimum number of locations, with additional awards at higher levels. For chasers,

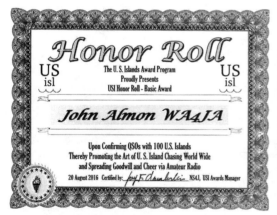

The US Islands Award Program offers the basic Honor Roll certificate for confirming contacts with 100 US islands in the program. Additional awards are available for higher levels.

World Wide Flora and Fauna is an international program, and a number of countries offer awards. This certificate is for working 10 different OHFF locations in Finland.

Parks on the Air (POTA) concentrates on parks and other natural areas in the United States and offers awards at various levels for chasers and activators.

The Summits On The Air (SOTA) "Mountain Goat" award is earned by activators who collect 1000 points. Not a mountain climber? You can go for the "Shack Sloth" award by collecting 1000 points as a chaser.

the award is for contacting a minimum number of unique identifiers, with additional awards for contacting more. In some programs, awards are based on points assigned to each location and determined by degree of difficulty. Summits on the Air (SOTA), for example, assigns points based on the height of a summit.

To verify that you have contacted the required number of locations for an award, some programs require paper QSL cards for each contact. Some programs require submission of QSL cards. Others are on the honor system but may ask for QSLs if there are questions or concerns about your application. Some programs maintain a database that matches contacts in logs uploaded by activators and chasers. Only matched QSOs count for awards. Some programs base their awards on contacts appearing in an activator's log that is uploaded to a database (chasers do not upload logs; the contact must be good in the activator's log to count).

Each organization will have different requirements, so check out the rules for any programs that interest you. Awards are a fun way to reach new goals while operating portable. You will boost your chances of success by operating from locations that are part of an active program with chasers anxious for a contact.

Here are some established programs that offer awards:

- Amateur Radio Lighthouse Society (ARLHS): **arlhs.com.**
  Operate from lighthouses around the world. Awards for activators and chasers.
- Beaches on the Air (BOTA): **www.beachesontheair.com**. Operate

Not all Islands on the Air (IOTA) locations are in warm climates. Cezar, VE3LYC, traveled to the Canadian Arctic to activate NA-186, Fox Island in Nunavut. (Courtesy Cezar Trifu, VE3LYC)

Curt, W4LKR, traveled by kayak to activate Rock Island near Nashville, Tennessee, for the US Islands Awards Program. (Courtesy Curt Walker, W4LKR)

portable from beaches around the world. Awards for activators and chasers.

- Islands on the Air (IOTA): **www.rsgbiota.org.** Operate from islands around the world. Awards for chasers; sponsors annual IOTA contest.
- Mines on the Air (MOTA): **minesontheair.com**. Operate near mines around the United States.
- Mobile Amateur Radio Awards Club (MARAC): **www.marac.org**. Resources for those interested in county hunting. Issues MARAC awards and supports the *CQ* Magazine USA-CA award.
- Parks on the Air (POTA): **parksontheair.com.** Operate from parks, national forests, wildlife refuges and other natural areas throughout the United States. Awards for activators and chasers.
- Summits on the Air (SOTA): **www.sota.org.uk.** Operate from summits worldwide. Higher summits are worth more points. Awards

for activators and chasers.

- US Islands Awards Program (USI): **usislands.org.** Operate from river, lake, and shore islands throughout the United States. Awards for activators and chasers; sponsors annual QSO party.
- World Wide Flora and Fauna (WWFF): **wwff.co.** Operate from parks, national forests, wildlife refuges and other natural areas worldwide. Awards for activators and chasers.
- World Wide Flora and Fauna in the United States (WWFF-KFF): **wwffkff.wordpress.com.** United States chapter of WWFF. Awards for activators and chasers.
- World Castles Award (COTA): **wcagroup.org.** Operate from castles and other important historical structures around the world. Awards for activators and chasers.

Contests and On-Air Operating Events

Although you can operate portable in any contest (and contests can be a good source of contacts if you're out on a weekend and not finding many chasers), there are a number of events throughout the year of special interest to portable operators. Some of the events listed here are mainly for portable operators, while others include special categories for portables or mobiles as well as the normal categories for home stations.

ARRL Field Day, an annual event since 1933, is the biggest operating event of the year. The purpose of Field Day is to set up a temporary station away from the home or club station and host an open house for the public to see Amateur Radio in action. Emergency power is often used, including generators, batteries, and solar power. These temporary stations set up antennas and radios with the purpose of contacting other Field Day operations or home stations to practice message handling and emergency communication in less than ideal conditions. Field Day offers a wide variety of portable and mobile entry categories ranging from QRP one-person operations to high-power club setups with

State QSO parties rely on portable, mobile, and rover stations to activate rare counties. For the 2016 Illinois QSO Party, Sterling, NØSSC; Kyle, NØKTK; Chris, WX5CW; Justin, KEØHXL; and Kevin, KØKEV set up at a state park on the Jefferson and Franklin county lines. This portable operating team is quite active in state QSO parties.

ARRL Field Day combines portable operating with a chance to show off Amateur Radio to the general public. Here one of the stations at Field Day site of the Huntsville Amateur Radio Club is visited by a group of teachers from the nearby US Space and Rocket Center Space Camp. (William Martin, KK4FDF, photo)

10 or more stations operating simultaneously.

Be sure to study the information for each event on the sponsor's website. There may be more than one entry class, each with its own set of guidelines and restrictions. For example, the low power or QRP class in some events may allow 5 W, while others allow up to 10 W.

You don't need any special equipment for portable contest operation, but if you are able to bring a computer for logging contacts it is beneficial to use special contest logging software such as *N1MM+ Logger* (**www.n1mm. hamdocs.com**) or *N3FJP Amateur Contact Log* (**www. n3fjp.com**). Contest software can help you keep track of your score and avoid duplicate contacts, which don't count.

Jamboree on the Air (JOTA) and special events are not contests, but they afford portable

A portable operating event in January? Must be Winter Field Day. (Photo credit: Julian, OH8STN)

Mountaintops are ideal locations for VHF/UHF contest operating. David, W4DVE, camped out on top of Davis Peak near Portland, Oregon, to win the Single Operator, Portable category in an ARRL VHF contest. (David Reindl, W4DVE, photo)

operators an opportunity to demonstrate ham radio to the general public. JOTA combines scouting and ham radio over a weekend where scouts can get on the air under supervision of a licensed amateur and talk to hams or other scouts. Special event stations are often set up at fairs, parades, and other community events. That not only gives hams worldwide an opportunity to learn about the event, but also gives amateurs a chance to publicize ham radio to visitors attending the event.

Here are some contests and on-air events that cater to portable or mobile operators:

- Adventure Radio Society: **arsqrp.blogspot.com**. Sponsors contests for operating portable with low power.
- ARRL Field Day: **www.arrl.org/field-day**. Thousands of clubs and individuals set up portable stations for this annual 24-hour on-air event the fourth weekend of June.
- ARRL VHF Contests: **www.arrl.org/contests**. ARRL sponsors several VHF/UHF contests throughout the year that offer Portable (10 W or less) and Rover (operate from multiple grid squares) categories.
- Jamboree on the Air (JOTA): **www.scouting.org/jota.aspx**. Annual worldwide event combining ham radio and scouting. Amateurs set up stations, often portable, and get scouts on the air.
- Radio Direction Finding (RDF): **www.homingin.com**. Resources

Frank, NF8M (left), and Josh Pratt had a great time during Jamboree On The Air, known simply as JOTA, at the Great Lakes Scout Radio Club station, WB8BSA, in Farmington Hills, Michigan. (Bob Pratt, WD8AQX, photo)

for radio direction finding, including local and international competitions.

• Rapid Deployment Amateur Radio (RaDAR): **radar-america. blogspot.com** and **groups.io/g/radar**. Set up a portable station and make a specified number of contacts, then tear down and set up again a specified distance away. Sponsors contests several times per year.

• Special Event Stations: **www.arrl.org/special-event-stations**. Operations, often portable, commemorating local, regional, and national events. Special QSLs and certificate are typically available.

• State QSO parties: **www.contestcalendar.com/stateparties.html**. Most states have annual QSO parties, which are a great opportunity for portable and mobile operators to activate rare counties.

• Winter Field Day: **www.winterfieldday.com**. Sponsored by the Winter Field Day Association, this 24-hour event is held annually in January and offers categories for portable stations (outdoor and indoor), as well as home stations.

Andrea, K2EZ, is a frequent VHF/UHF rover from this well-equipped mobile station.
(Courtesy Andrea Slack, K2EZ)

Hams launch balloons with various payloads, including video transmitters and trackers. Bill, WB8ELK, demonstrates a fairly simple setup, a Mylar party balloon carrying a 12-gram Skytracker APRS tracker. Some ham high-altitude balloons carry much larger payloads to the edge of space. (Bev Teter, WB4ELK, photo)

Check out the Bicycle Mobile Hams of America website if you're interested in operating ham radio from your bike. Skyler, KDØWHB, has quite the bicycle mobile setup. (Courtesy Skyler Fennell, KDØWHB)

Portable Operating Clubs and Groups

One way to learn more about portable operating is to share your experiences with other hams who are interested in the same activity. These days there are a number of groups on social media such as Facebook, Yahoo Groups, and Groups.io for hams who like portable and mobile operating, operating outdoors, QRP, antennas, the various awards programs discussed earlier, and many other topics of interest. Try searching the web or the various social media sites for terms such as "ham radio outdoors" or "portable ham radio" and see what turns up.

There are also several websites and clubs for specific areas of interest to portable operators:

- Amateur Radio High Altitude Ballooning (ARHAB): **www.arhab.org**. Resources for those interested in launching and tracking Amateur Radio transmitters aboard high-altitude balloons.
- Bicycle Mobile Hams of America (BHMA): **bmha-hams.org**. For hams who operate their radios while bicycle mobile.

- QRP Amateur Radio Club International (QRP ARCI): **www.qrparci.org**. Resources for those interested in operating with QRP (5 W or less).
- RV Radio Network: **rvradionetwork.com**. Resources for those interested in operating from recreational vehicles.

Emergency Preparedness and Public Service Activities

When the power mains, telephones, and other normal communication channels are interrupted during a weather event or other disaster, hams with portable and mobile stations spring into action. They set up stations at Emergency Operation Centers (EOCs), Red Cross shelters, hospitals, and other key points to pass messages as needed. They may observe and report on hazardous weather conditions.

To participate effectively, hams need to join a local emergency preparedness group. The three organizations listed below all are well established, offer training and resources, and are integrated with other disaster response groups in the area. Training can include regular nets, simulated emergency exercises, and even communication support for local events such as parades and running races.

- ARRL Amateur Radio Emergency Service (ARES): **www.arrl.org/ares**. Resources and training for those interested in disaster response and public service communication.

Community events offer amateurs an opportunity to train for emergencies while serving their communities and demonstrating ham radio to the public. One of the largest such events is the annual New York City Marathon, where a large group of volunteers staff key points along the course. Here, members of the communication team staff a command center. From left to right: Harvey, WS2Q; Anthony, W2NET; Ray, K2NET, and Bob, K2RSB. (Courtesy Gordon Beattie, W2TTT)

- Community Emergency Response Team (CERT): **www.ready.gov/community-emergency-response-team**. Training in disaster preparedness and disaster response skills. Teams are organized at the local level.
- SKYWARN: **www.skywarn.org**. Training and resources for weather spotters who provide reports of severe and hazardous weather. Sponsored by the National Weather Service and often affiliated with local ARRL Amateur Radio Emergency Service groups.

Specialty Operating Activities

Although the activities listed below are not strictly portable activities, they offer opportunities to enhance portable operations. For example, you can use an APRS tracker as you travel to your site so that chasers can monitor your progress. Amateur satellites are a natural for portable operators because they can be accessed with a handheld antenna and VHF handheld radio. UHF and microwave contacts can be made over greater distances from locations high and in the clear, such as mountain summits.

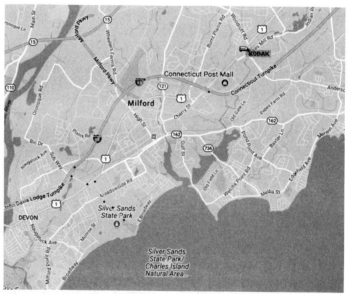

APRS is a great way for activators to let chasers see their progress toward a location. This screen from aprs.fi shows that Pete, KØBAK, has completed an activation from Silver Sands State Park in Connecticut and is heading for the next location.

Barry, VE4MA, operating portable on several microwave bands at 10 GHz and higher frequencies from Manitoba. (Barry Malowanchuk, VE4MA, photo)

- Automatic Packet Reporting System (APRS): **www.aprs.org**. Digital communications channel for ham radio, often used for tracking mobile and portable stations. Also see the APRS mapping site at **aprs.fi**.
- DX Expeditions: **www.ng3k.com/misc/adxo.html**. Calendar of upcoming DXpeditions to locations around the world.
- Microwave: **www.arrl.org/microwave.** Resources for those interested in operating on the UHF and microwave bands. Mountaintops, hills, and tall manmade structures are the best locations.
- Radio Amateur Satellite Corp. (AMSAT): **www.amsat.org**. Resources for those interested in operating through amateur satellites.

Multiple Programs

If you are operating portable in an area that has a site that qualifies for several different radio activities, you can operate dual and even triple activations from one area. An example is a SOTA summit that falls within a park that's on the Parks on the Air (POTA) list. You can submit logs to both programs for credit — just know the appropriate location identifiers.

Completing a dual activation can increase your potential contacts by

The low Earth orbit FM satellites are popular with portable operators. Ruth, KM4LAO is making contacts with a VHF FM handheld and a portable antenna for 2 meters and 70 centimeters. Courtesy Ruth Willet, KM4LAO)

Stuart, KB1HQS, operating from Mt Washington in New Hampshire, which qualifies for both Parks on the Air (POTA) and Summits on the Air (SOTA) activations at the same time. One portable expedition results in activating under two different programs.

attracting chasers from both groups (in this example, SOTA and POTA). Those who follow both groups will be even more motivated to work you as they can accumulate points for both activities simultaneously with one contact.

Publicizing Your Portable Operation

How can you increase the awareness about your upcoming portable operation? Utilizing social media such as Facebook is one example. There are many groups on Facebook that are specific to different portable radio activities. Group members often announce upcoming activations, and if they have cell coverage they provide updates on the way to, and even during their operations. Group members also announce ("spot") activations that they work on the air.

Facebook is also an excellent way to advertise your upcoming events to all of your Amateur Radio friends. Other popular social media resources include Twitter, Instagram, Reddit, and YouTube.

Do you have a website or a blog? Creating an entry describing your upcoming adventures is an easy way to share the details of your trip. Another option to increase awareness is to create an e-mail list or e-mail newsletter that you send out to your amateur friends. On my website I have an option for visitors to submit their e-mail addresses so they can receive my e-mails that promote my upcoming portable activations. Leveraging social media and the internet to help promote your next radio trip can increase your chances of making contacts and new friends in the amateur community.

Facebook groups, such as these for the World Wide Flora and Fauna in the United States (WWFF-KFF) and Parks on the Air programs, are a great place to publicize your activation.

Chapter 9

Accessories and Tools

Over time, as you spend more time operating portable you will start to recognize situations where certain accessories and tools are needed for a successful operation. Many of these items you will acquire as you gain experience in the field with your particular setup. This chapter lists many items that I have found useful, and that you should consider adding to your gear as necessary.

An important point is that you should acquire items *as you need them*. Doing this will cut out unnecessary purchases of items that you may find you really don't need.

HF Radio

Amateur Radio License — While not required by the FCC, having a copy of your license can be helpful in explaining your actions to public officials while in a public area. Laminating your license to protect it from the elements is a good idea. If you need an extra copy to carry, check out **www.arrl.org/obtain-license-copy**.

Audio cables — High quality audio cables for interfacing your voice recorder and any laptop connections for digital work.

Bag ID tags — Especially helpful when traveling to identify your gear bags. These don't have to ham specific; regular luggage tags can be used as well.

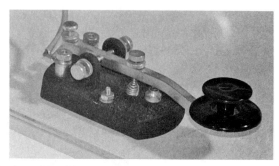

CW paddles/straight key — Always good to have along even if you plan to mostly operate using SSB or FM. Sometimes CW is more effective with a small station or during poor conditions.

Earbuds or headphones — Ear buds are cheap (< $10) and it's always good to have a second pair as a backup. Over-the-ear headphones will block out more noise, but take more room in a backpack.

Frequency cheat sheet — Whether purchased or homemade, a sheet showing the band segments and a list of popular frequencies is always good to have on hand for reference.

Hydrosorbent OSG-40 Silica Gel Rechargeable Desiccant — If your radio is stored in a sealed container, keeping moisture levels to a minimum is crucial. Many rechargeable desiccants can be dried out in the oven.

Logbook and pen(s) or pencil(s) — Even if you use a computer or tablet/smartphone for logging, it's a good idea to bring old-fashioned pencil and paper as a backup. If you're going to be out in the elements for a while, consider waterproof versions.

Microphone — Your radio probably came with a hand mic...don't forget to bring it! Consider a headset mic if you are not carrying your gear too far.

Paint brush or photography dust brush — Keeping dust out of your expensive electronics is important in protecting your expensive investment.

MENU OPERATION

	Menu Item	Function	Available Values	Default
19	CW PADDLE	Select the keyer paddle's wiring configuration	NORMAL/REVERSE	NORMAL
20	CW PITCH	Setting of the pitch of the CW sidetone, BFO offset, and CW filter center frequencies	300 ~ 1000 Hz	700 Hz
21	CW SPEED	Set the sending speed for the built-in Electronic keyer	4wpm ~ 60 wpm/ 20cpm ~ 300 cpm	12 wpm (60 cpm)
22	CW WEIGHT	Set the Dot:Dash ratio for the built-in electronic keyer	1:2.5 ~ 1:4.5	1:3.0
23	DCS CODE	Setting the DCS code	104 Std DCS codes	023
24	DIG DISP	Define the displayed frequency offset during DIG (USER-L or USER-U) mode operation	-3000 ~ +3000 Hz	0 Hz
25	DIG MIC	Adjust the audio input level from terminal equipment (such as a TNC or PSK-31 sound card) during DIG (Digital) mode operation	0 ~ 100	50
26	DIG MODE	Select the mode and sideband (if applicable) in the DIG (Digital) mode	RTTY/ PSK31-L/PSK31-U/ USER-L/USER-U	RTTY
27	DIG SHIFT	Define the carrier frequency offset during DIG (USER-L or USER-U) mode operation	-3000 ~ +3000 Hz	0 Hz
28	EMERGENCY	Enable Tx/Rx operation on the Alaska Emergency Channel, 5167.5 kHz (USA Version only)	OFF/ON	OFF

Radio manuals — Keep a hardcopy collection of your radios manuals for any field reference. Even if you don't carry the entire manual, instructions for adjusting menus or resetting the radio may come in handy.

Voice recorder — Small digital recorders are ideal for recording QSOs or making notes. The Sony ICD PX-370 is a proven product.

VHF/UHF Handheld Radio

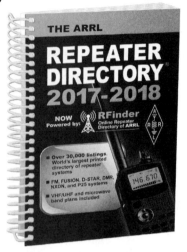

ARRL Repeater Directory — If you're operating away from your local area, it's always a good idea to have a listing of area repeaters. Not only will this help you find contacts, but also can be invaluable if you run into trouble.

Charger and/or spare battery — The batteries in today's handhelds last a very long time, but if you will be out for a while it's a good idea to carry a spare battery and cables to charge your radio from both ac and dc power sources.

External antenna — The short flexible antenna that came with your handheld is okay for local communication, but you can extend your range with a collapsible whip or other higher-performance aftermarket antenna. Better yet, carry a dual band J-Pole. Some designs are made from 300 ohm twinlead and roll up into a small and very lightweight package.

Speaker/microphone — Sometimes it's more convenient to set down your radio or leave it on your belt and use an accessory speaker/ microphone.

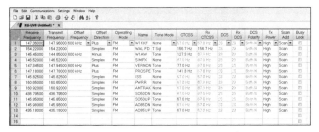

	Receive Frequency	Transmit Frequency	Offset Frequency	Offset Direction	Operating Mode	Name	Tone Mode	CTCSS	Rx CTCSS	DCS	Rx DCS	DCS Polarity	Tx Power	Scan Add	Busy Lock
1	147.36000	147.96000	600 kHz	Plus	FM	W1KKF	None	67.0 Hz	67.0 Hz	23	23	Both N	High	Scan	
2	154.22000	154.22000		Simplex	FM	WAL FD	T Sql	156.7 Hz	156.7 Hz	23	23	Both N	High	Scan	
3	145.45000	144.85000	600 kHz	Minus	FM	W1AW	Tone	127.3 Hz	67.0 Hz	23	23	Both N	High	Scan	
4	146.52000	146.52000		Simplex	FM	SIMPX	None	67.0 Hz	67.0 Hz	23	23	Both N	High	Scan	
5	147.34500	147.94500	600 kHz	Plus	FM	VERNON	Tone	77.0 Hz	67.0 Hz	23	23	Both N	High	Scan	
6	147.18000	147.78000	600 kHz	Plus	FM	PROSPE	Tone	141.3 Hz	67.0 Hz	23	23	Both N	High	Scan	
7	145.82500	145.82500		Simplex	FM	ISS	None	67.0 Hz	67.0 Hz	23	23	Both N	High	Scan	
8	160.65000	160.65000		Simplex	FM	PWRR	None	67.0 Hz	67.0 Hz	23	23	Both N	High	Scan	
9	160.92000	160.92000		Simplex	FM	AMTRAK	None	67.0 Hz	67.0 Hz	23	23	Both N	High	Scan	
10	436.79500	436.79500		Simplex	FM	SO50DN	None	67.0 Hz	67.0 Hz	23	23	Both N	High	Scan	
11	145.85000	145.85000		Simplex	FM	SO50UP	Tone	67.0 Hz	67.0 Hz	23	23	Both N	High	Scan	
12	145.98000	145.98000		Simplex	FM	AO85DN	None	67.0 Hz	67.0 Hz	23	23	Both N	High	Scan	
13	435.18000	435.18000		Simplex	FM	AO85UP	Tone	67.0 Hz	67.0 Hz	23	23	Both N	High	Scan	
14															
15															

USB programming cable and software — If you find entering new repeaters manually to be tedious, use your laptop to streamline the process. Many radio manufacturers offer accessory cables and free software, and RT Systems offers programming kits for nearly every popular model.

Power

Anderson Powerpole cable for your radio — If your radio doesn't already have Anderson Powerpole connectors installed, adding them is a good idea for power standardization.

Anderson Power Pole splitter — This is a convenient way to power several devices from one battery or power source.

Anderson Powerpole polarity checker — It's always a good idea to check the polarity of Powerpole connectors before using them for the first time to make sure they are wired the same way as the rest of your gear.

Cell phone/tablet and USB cables — Considering the number of battery-operated accessories charged via USB cables today, be sure to add the appropriate USB cables for all of your electronic devices.

CO (carbon monoxide) detector — If running a generator, a CO detector is an absolute must.

Extension cable/power strip — If you are using commercial ac power or a generator, you'll probably need to plug in several pieces of equipment. Verify that the extension cable and power strip are rated for the amount of current you will be using.

Spare spark plugs, oil change kit — Refer to your generator manual for recommended oil weight and spark plug replacements.

Computer

Chargers — Having the ability to charge your laptop with both dc and ac is smart emergency management pre-planning. If you are using a cell phone or tablet, bring along a USB cable and ac charger to top off the battery or run from external power.

Collapsible chair/table — Using a computer is much more comfortable if you have a small table and chair, rather than sitting on the ground.

Software — Keep a spare USB thumb drive with a bootable operating system and a backup of your often-used ham radio software and log data files.

Spare laptop battery — A good tip is to label each battery so you can keep track of your batteries and the state of their charge.

Sunshade — If you are accustomed to using your computer indoors, you may be surprised how difficult it is to read the screen in sunlight. A laptop sunshade is useful for both mobile and outdoor operating in bright sunlight.

Antennas

Antenna analyzer — An antenna analyzer is very handy for adjusting multiband antennas or diagnosing antenna problems. Be sure to bring spare batteries.

Coaxial cable — 25-foot lengths of RG-8X or RG-58 coax can be joined with barrel connectors to make any needed length. Consider RG-213 or RG-8 size coax for higher power and/or longer run applications. Short jumpers may also be needed to connect your radio to an external antenna tuner, SWR meter or other accessory.

Baluns — Your antenna may require a 4:1 or 1:1 balun.

BNC-to-binding post RF adapter — This is a super useful RF adapter that can be used as part of an antenna setup or to interconnect with coax with no RF connector.

Cable ties — Cable ties that come in various colors and use hook-and-loop fasteners are handy for securing wires, temporarily hanging antennas, and other uses. Plastic zip ties are cheap and good for one-time use.

Ground stakes — For anchoring guy lines and antenna support ropes.

Insulators — You never know when you might have to build or repair an antenna in the field, so carry a few spare insulators.

RF adapters — Be sure to carry a variety of RF adapters that can be used with other antennas and radio systems that may differ from your RF connector configuration.

Rope — Paracord, small diameter nylon line (mason's line), and ⅛ inch diameter polypropylene line are all useful for guy lines, throw lines, and antenna supports.

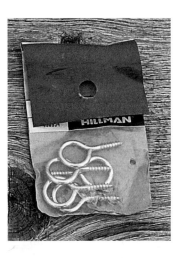

Screw eye hooks — Sometimes you just need a small hook to attach a lightweight antenna, and these come in very handy.

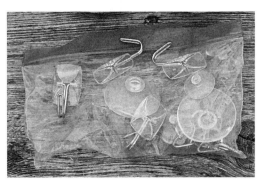

Suction cups with hooks — These are useful for installing small antennas temporarily on glass windows.

Throw weights — Carry several throw weights for tossing antenna support lines over convenient branches. Lead fishing sinkers, tennis balls with weights inside, and a Weaver 12-ounce leather throw weight are all useful.

Wire — Having spare wire of various gauges that can be used for field expedient antennas or power hookups is always a good idea. Stranded wire is easier to store and handle than solid.

Wrap strap — For a quick reusable mast attachment, try an adjustable plastic strap such as the Wrap-n-Strap from Startech.

Tools

You won't be bringing your tool chest from home, but some of the following tools can be helpful depending on the details of your activation.

- Crimpers — coax connector, Powerpole, wire terminal
- Cordless drill, drill bits
- Desoldering pump ("solder sucker") or braid
- Dummy load
- Hammer/mallet
- Measuring tape

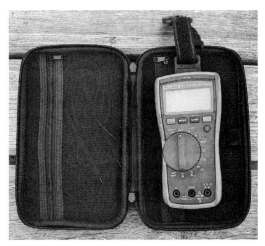

- Multimeter

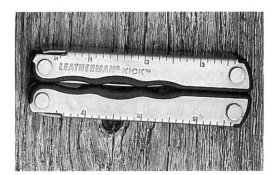

- Multitool
- Screwdrivers — Phillips and slotted, miniature/jeweler's

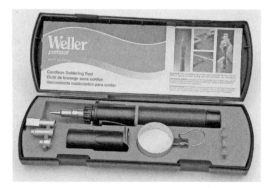

- Soldering iron — portable butane iron with spare butane and solder
- Pliers — standard, locking, needle nose, forceps/tweezer
- Powerpole crimper
- Utility knife

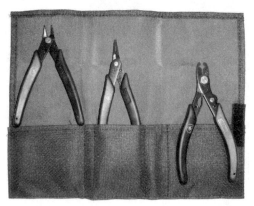

- Wire cutters, strippers
- Wrenches — open end and box, standard/metric, adjustable

Miscellaneous

- Coax sealing tape or butyl rubber electrical tape
- Dielectric grease for waterproofing connectors or improving electrical connections
- Duct tape
- Electrical tape — good quality, such as Scotch Super 33+
- Flagging tape, high visibility, for wires and ropes

- Headlamp and flashlight
- Heat shrink tubing
- Pen, permanent marker
- Stainless steel hose clamps
- Terminals and wire connectors (butt, ring, spade lugs - crimp type)

Chapter 10

Logging Contacts

While no longer legally required by the FCC, the practice of logging your contacts is still a common practice in the amateur community. By keeping a log, you have a record of your transmissions and interesting contacts, as well as a glimpse into propagation trends. Similar to the home station, there are many different ways to log your contacts. The most common ways are written (paper) and electronic logging.

Paper Logging

Paper and pencil (or pen) logging is the easiest and most reliable way to record your contacts. No power is needed to log, but the downside is that all data, including date and time, must be noted by the operator. (Date, time, and other information may be entered automatically with an electronic logging application.) Regardless of your logging preference, having a small paper log with your gear may come in useful as a backup if your primary electronic logging software fails.

The log can be a simple piece of scrap paper or a deluxe waterproof, lined field notebook. If you opt for something more than a scrap of paper, here are a few alternatives:

- ARRL Minilog: **www.arrl.org/shop/minilog/**
- ARRL Weatherproof Minilog: **www.arrl.org/shop/All-Weather-Amateur-Radio-Minilog/**
- Field Notes Expedition: **fieldnotesbrand.com/products/expedition**
- Rite in the Rain: **www.riteintherain.com**

A pencil is often used for a writing utensil. Regardless of the weather conditions, a pencil will always work. You can always keep it sharp and usable if you carry a knife or a pencil sharpener. Pencils are also cheap, plentiful, and lightweight. A golf pencil works well due to its small size.

Pens are another option. Many manufacturers offer pens that will write in all conditions, even upside down. One compact and rugged high-end option is the Field Notes Fisher Space Pen (**fieldnotesbrand. com/products/space-pen**).

For those not going into extreme environments, the readily available Uni-Ball Power Tank pen

ARRL's compact Minilog is designed for mobile and portable operators. There is also a weatherproof version available.

A plastic clipboard can be modified to secure a paper logbook and pencil, radio, and CW paddle. (Courtesy David Weingart, K2FI)

works well, with minimal ink smearing. There is nothing more frustrating than logging contacts, only to have them smear into an unreadable mess. Whatever pen/pencil and paper combo you use, be sure to see how well they work together before recording call signs. Also, try testing them in damp conditions like you might encounter in the field.

Another good tip for field use is to "dummy cord" your pen to your notebook so you don't lose it. In the field, I find it is easy to set a pen down to change bands or tune an antenna, only to realize I lost the pen somewhere on the ground. With your pen attached to your logbook, you will always know where to find it. An easy way to do this is to heat shrink small diameter nylon line to the pen. On the other end, attach the line to a large rubber band that fits around your notebook. This flexible setup allows you to remove the attached pen so that you can easily replace it as needed.

Another enhancement to the written log is a plastic clipboard that holds your paper and pen. This board can be commercially bought or home made with a variety of binder clips. The benefit of a plastic clipboard is you have a sturdy writing platform with space to record calls and a place to store your pen. There are many choices available from The Clipboard Shop (**clipboards.com**) — look for the Small and Mini sizes.

For those not needing a lightweight paper logging application, a dry erase board is another option, especially for mobile operators. If you need to reference location designators or other often repeated information, a dry erase board is useful tool to jot notes quickly. Even if you don't have a dry erase board with you, assuming you are stationary you could use your car windshield for a temporary dry-erase writing surface. Of course, you want to erase the contents before driving due to the limited visibility safety factor.

Recording Your Contacts

Before we get into electronic logging with a tablet or computer, using an audio or video recorder during your contacts should be mentioned. There are times you may want to record audio/video from QSOs for a backup copy of your conversations after being on the air.

A handheld digital voice recorder, such as the Sony ICD PX-370 is a very versatile tool to have in the field radio pack. Not only can you record QSOs, but it can also be used to quickly record notes about brief contacts and field equipment configurations. Operating mobile, this tool comes in very handy for hands-free logging using the voice operated recording function.

For those with smartphones, a variety of apps can be used to record audio. Here are a couple of options:

• Voice Record Pro (iOS): **itunes.apple.com/us/app/voice-record-pro/id546983235?mt=8**

• Smart Recorder (Android): **play.google.com/store/apps/details?id=com.andrwq.recorder&hl=en**

Many current smartphones and compact cameras will record video as well as audio. If you record videos of your portable operations, the camera can be set up to get direct inline audio from your radio using a headphone splitter or line-out port.

A compact digital recorder can be used to log contacts or record many hours of on-air operating.

Logging Apps and Software

The last method is electronic logging, which covers a wide span of software, hardware, and power requirements.

Smartphones and Tablets

The simplest setup is a smartphone or tablet with a logging app. Having your cell phone and logging app with you all the time is useful for quick contacts as they arise. With a touch of a button you can log QSOs, with the app automatically recording the date and time (UTC) of the contact, giving you quick and accurate details of the QSO for later uploads. One downside of smartphones or tablets is the small screens and virtual

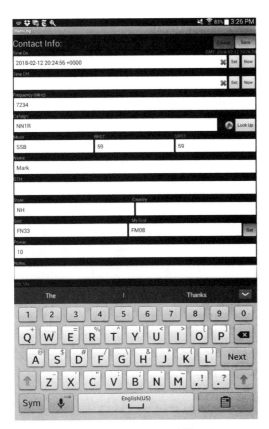

HamLog is a popular logging app for iOS and Android devices. It automatically records date and time from the device, pre-populates the signal report fields with 59 or 599, and remembers the band and mode last used. If you are running stations in the field, you just need to enter a call sign and location or other information pertinent to that contact.

HamLog also includes a lengthy list of tools and calculators that may be of use in the field. Some of these require an internet connection.

keyboards, which can make data entry cumbersome. Adding a Bluetooth wireless keyboard and mouse can make data entry easier.

Most logging apps are inexpensive, with the cost primarily residing in the hardware needed to run them. If you already own a smartphone or tablet, the cost is negligible. Popular apps for smartphones and tablets include:

- *HamLog* (iOS): **pignology.net/hamlog.html**
- *HamLog* (Android): **play.google.com/store/apps/details?id=com.n3wg.hamlog&hl=en**
- *RUMlogNG2go* (iOS): **itunes.apple.com/de/app/rumlogng2go/id1005575164?mt=8**

Logging Apps on Smartphones/Tablets

Pros:
- Hardware (phone/tablet) commonly owned
- Inexpensive apps
- Simple user interface
- Can link with external keyboard
- Devices are compact in size and weight
- Low power requirements
- Easy to charge with 5 V dc external power sources
- All devices have Wi-Fi, but some may not have GPS or cell service

Cons:
- Small screen, may be hard to read for some
- Apps may have limited capability compared to regular computer software
- Device may be fragile or damaged by environmental conditions
- Virtual keyboard can make it difficult to enter data
- May be difficult to upload data to external sources

A custom SOTA template for *HamLog*.

The *RUMlogNG2go* for iOS logging app. It can share files with the *RUMlogNG* for Mac computers.

RUMlogNG2go **includes a Pileup mode for streamlined data entry.**

Some logging apps also allow you to create custom logging templates for specific activities. For example, Vance, N3VEM, has created a custom Parks on the Air template using *HamLog* (**www.n3vem. com/blog/wwff-logging-more-with-hamlog**). Other useful options within HamLog include DX spotting/cluster connectivity, grid square calculators and tools, band plans, and antenna length calculations. (Some of these tools require an internet connection.)

How do you transfer these logs to other devices or applications once created? The app exports logs in the standard ADIF format (.adi or .adif), which can be uploaded directly to Logbook of the World, award sponsors, or to a home computer for integration with personal logging programs.

Laptop Computer

The most common way people record their logs electronically is using laptops or home desktop computers. This method has been in use since computers started appearing in shacks during the 1980s. As a result, there is a wide variety of software, both free and paid, available to the amateur community.

While many operators use desktop computers at

Using a laptop for logging offers the opportunity to use the same software as used at home, as well as the option to run additional software such as digital mode applications.

Logging on a Laptop

Pros:

- Can use full logging software that the operator is familiar with at home; more features available
- Can interface radio and logging software using serial or USB ports
- Can run other software such as such as digital mode programs (*fldigi*, *WSJT-X*, etc)
- Ability to run multiple programs at once due to the higher processing power
- Better graphics
- Storage capability much higher
- Can be "hot spotted" (interfaced with a cell phone or other cellular hot spot to give the operator internet access)
- Replaceable batteries for a quick power swap

Cons:

- Higher power/battery requirements
- Power source may require ac to charge; dc (cigarette plugs) chargers available
- Heavier, larger form factor
- Can produce a lot of heat
- More vulnerable to environmental conditions
- More complex operating system
- Hardware cost can be higher, depending on the manufacturer

home, with few exceptions (Emergency Operations Centers, for example) portable operators prefer using a laptop because of portability. Using a laptop offers a wider selection of logging software with more capabilities than smartphone/tablet apps. There is also the familiarity factor of using the same software at home and in the field, reducing the need to learn a new logging program. Other useful Amateur Radio software such as digital decoding and propagation software can be run on a laptop as well.

Popular logging programs include:

- *DXLab*: **www.dxlabsuite.com**
- *Fast Log Entry* (*FLE*): **www.df3cb.com/fle**
- *Log4OM*: **www.log4om.com**
- *Logger32*: **www.logger32.net/index.html**
- *MacLoggerDX*: **dogparksoftware.com/MacLoggerDX.html**
- *N1MM+ Logger* (in DXpedition mode): **n1mm.hamdocs.com**
- *N3FJP Amateur Contact Log*: **www.n3fjp.com**

If all you need is basic logging, bringing along a laptop might be more trouble than it is worth. The decision comes to what software you need, the battery power available to keep it running, and the type of environment you will be operating in. There is no "right answer" when it comes to logging electronically.

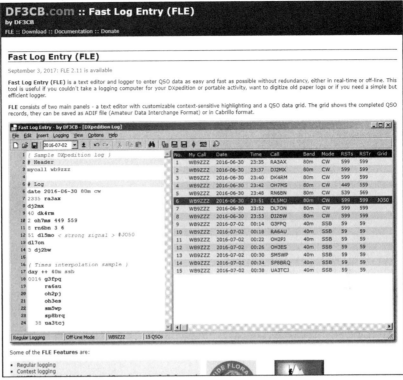

DF3CB's *Fast Log Entry* (*FLE*) is a *Windows* logging program that includes special features for SOTA, WWFF, and contest operation.

Microcontrollers

Until recently, logging electronically mostly consisted of using software on home computers. Along with the smartphone and tablet, there is a new class of logging electronics. The popular Raspberry Pi and Arduino microcontrollers can be used for ham radio logging applications. Their small footprint and low power requirements make them ideal candidates for logging in the field. Here are a couple of resources to check out:

• Raspberry Pi: **thenextweb.com/shareables/2017/03/24/ handheld-linux-pc-raspberry-pi-iphone/**

• Arduino: **www.tucsonhamradio.org/ovarc_docs/ ovarc-2013-11-15.pdf**

Appendix

Online Resources

This Appendix lists links for a number of websites, blogs, and suppliers that I have found helpful in assembling and using my portable station.

Blogs, Websites and Social Media

AD5A, Michael:
ad5aradio.blogspot.com/

GØPOT, Michael:
peanutpower.co.uk

K5ACL, SignalSearch:
www.k5acl.net

K9ARV, Tony:
www.youtube.com/channel/UCDuqrE6euNFcxJL520jKmsA

KØMOS, Matt:
www.schnizer.com/SOTAblog/

KØNR, Bob:
www.k0nr.com/wordpress/

KB1HQS, Stuart:
kb1hqs.com

KD8RTT, Tony:
www.youtube.com/user/12milluz/videos

KE6MT, Rex:
www.ke6mt.us/

KG4AKV, Spacecomms:
spacecomms.wordpress.com

KG6HQD, Jerry:
www.youtube.com/channel/UCFupjnMVW-4n3Gl3NWjkSaQ

JP1QEC, Akira:
www.youtube.com/channel/UChd7Khi_Z_sMjabixjz-p5g

MØJCQ, James:
www.hamblog.co.uk

N4CCB, Cliff (QRP School):
www.youtube.com/channel/UCEINppMdTOP8apApXXhZLCQ

N9YO, Tommy:
> **www.youtube.com/channel/UCQfwjjXcnW1hE4v2OTKgeFw/videos**

NØSSC, Sterling:
> **n0ssc.com**

OH8STN, Survival Tech Nord:
> **oh8stn.org**

VK3YE, Peter:
> **www.youtube.com/user/vk3ye**

W6PNG, Paul:
> **w6png.wordpress.com/**

WGØAT, Steve:
> **www.youtube.com/channel/UCe51a2pmXf7eubW7o7cM-nA**

Antennas

AlexLoop:
> **www.alexloop.com**

Alpha Antennas:
> **alphaantenna.com**

Arrow Antennas:
> **www.arrowantennas.com**

Buddipole:
> **www.buddipole.com**

Chameleon Antenna:
> **chameleonantenna.com**

Coax calculator:
> **www.timesmicrowave.com/calculator/**

Diamond Antenna:
> **www.diamondantenna.net**

Elk Antennas:
> **elkantennas.com**

Emtech:
> **steadynet.com/emtech/**

LDG Electronics:
> **www.ldgelectronics.com**

LNR Precision:
> **www.lnrprecision.com**

MFJ:
> **www.mfjenterprises.com**

MyAntennas:
> **myantennas.com**

Pacific Antenna:
> **www.qrpkits.com/sota.html**

PackTenna:
   packtenna.com
QRP Guys:
   qrpguys.apps-1and1.com/end-fed-half-wave-sota-antenna-tuner
SOTABEAMS:
   www.sotabeams.co.uk
Super Antenna:
   www.newsuperantenna.com
Wolf River Coils:
   wolfrivercoils.com

Hiking and Camping

AT Hiker Planner:
   www.postholer.com/planner/Appalachian-Trail/3
Backcountry:
   www.backcountry.com
Backpacking Light:
   backpackinglight.com
HikerAlert Emergency Alert App:
   hikeralert.com
L.L. Bean:
   www.llbean.com
PCT Planner:
   www.pctplanner.com
REI Co-op:
   www.rei.com
Sierra Trading Post:
   www.sierratradingpost.com
Ten Essentials:
   www.rei.com/learn/expert-advice/ten-essentials.html
WhiteBlaze:
   www.whiteblaze.net

Logging

Arduino:
   www.tucsonhamradio.org/ovarc_docs/ovarc-2013-11-15.pdf
ARRL Weatherproof Minilog:
   www.arrl.org/shop/All-Weather-Amateur-Radio-Minilog
Clipboard Shop:
   clipboards.com

DXLab:

www.dxlabsuite.com

Field Notes Expedition:

fieldnotesbrand.com/products/expedition

Field Notes Fisher Space Pen:

fieldnotesbrand.com/products/space-pen

HamLog (iOS):

pignology.net/hamlog.html

HamLog (Android):

play.google.com/store/apps/details?id=com.n3wg.hamlog&hl=en

Logger32:

www.logger32.net/index.html

MacLoggerDX:

www.dogparksoftware.com/MacLoggerDX.html

N1MM+ Logger:

n1mm.hamdocs.com

N3FJP Amateur Contact Log:

www.n3fjp.com

Raspberry Pi:

thenextweb.com/shareables/2017/03/24/
handheld-linux-pc-raspberry-pi-iphone/

Rite in the Rain:

www.riteintherain.com

RUMlogNG2go (iOS):

itunes.apple.com/de/app/rumlogng2go/id1005575164?mt=8

Smart Recorder (Android):

play.google.com/store/apps/details?id=com.andrwq.recorder&hl=en

Voice Record Pro (iOS):

itunes.apple.com/us/app/voice-record-pro/id546983235?mt=8

Navigation

Bureau of Land Management Maps:

www.blm.gov/maps

DeLorme Atlas & Gazetteer Paper Maps series of books:

buy.garmin.com/en-US/US/p/575993

Gaia GPS Navigation App:

www.gaiagps.com

Gmap4 web application:

mappingsupport.com/p/gmap4-free-online-topo-maps.html

GPS File Depot:

www.gpsfiledepot.com

GPS Babel:
www.gpsbabel.org
Identify mountains from other summits:
www.heywhatsthat.com
National Park Service app:
www.nps.gov/subjects/digital/nps-apps.htm
OpenSignal:
opensignal.com
Spotwalla:
spotwalla.com
US Forest Service Map:
www.fs.fed.us/visit/maps

On the Air Activities

Adventure Radio Society:
arsqrp.blogspot.com
Amateur Radio High Altitude Ballooning (ARHAB):
www.arhab.org
Amateur Radio Lighthouse Society (ARLHS):
arlhs.com
ARRL Amateur Radio Emergency Service (ARES):
www.arrl.org/ares
Automatic Packet Reporting System (APRS):
www.aprs.org
DX Expeditions:
www.ng3k.com/misc/adxo.html
ARRL Field Day:
www.arrl.org/field-day
ARRL resources:
www.arrl.org/microwave
ARRL VHF Contests:
www.arrl.org/contests
Beaches on the Air (BOTA):
www.beachesontheair.com
Bicycle Mobile Hams of America (BHMA):
bmha-hams.org
Community Emergency Response Team (CERT):
www.ready.gov/community-emergency-response-team
Islands on the Air (IOTA):
www.rsgbiota.org
Jamboree on the Air (JOTA):
www.scouting.org/jota.aspx

MailChimp:
   mailchimp.com
Mines on the Air (MOTA):
   minesontheair.com
Mobile Amateur Radio Awards Club (MARAC):
   www.marac.org
Parks on the Air (POTA):
   parksontheair.com
QRP Amateur Radio Club International (QRP ARCI):
   www.qrparci.org
Radio Amateur Satellite Corp. (AMSAT):
   www.amsat.org
Radio Direction Finding (RDF):
   www.homingin.com
Rapid Deployment Amateur Radio (RaDAR):
   radar-america.blogspot.com and groups.io/g/radar
Revue Newsletter:
   www.getrevue.co
RV Radio Network:
   rvradionetwork.com
SKYWARN:
   www.skywarn.org
Special Event Stations:
   www.arrl.org/special-event-stations
State QSO parties:
   www.contestcalendar.com/stateparties.html
Summits on the Air (SOTA):
   www.sota.org.uk
US Islands Awards Program (USI):
   usislands.org
Winter Field Day:
   www.winter eldday.com
World Wide Flora and Fauna (WWFF):
   wwff.co
World Wide Flora and Fauna in the United States (WWFF-KFF):
   wwffkff.wordpress.com
World Castles Award (COTA):
   wcagroup.org

Mobile

ARRL Equipment Insurance:
www.arrlinsurance.com
ARRL marine mobile:
www.arrl.org/maritime-mobile-operation-in-international-waters
ARRL mobile stations:
www.arrl.org/mobile-stations
KØBG:
www.k0bg.com
Governors Highway Safety Association:
www.ghsa.org/state-laws/ issues/Distracted-Driving
Maritime Mobile Service Network:
www.mmsn.org

Power Sources

Amp hour calculator:
www.4sqrp.com/Battery_Capacity/index. php
Bioenno LiFePO4 batteries:
www.bioennopower.com
BuddiPole PowerMini Controller:
www.buddipole.com/powermini.html
GENASUN MPPT Controllers:
genasun.com
Goal Zero:
www.goalzero.com
Hardened Power Systems:
www.portableuniversalpower.com
Honda Portable Generators:
powerequipment.honda.com/generators
MFJ Enterprises:
www.mfjenterprises.com
PowerFilm:
www.power filmsolar.com
Powerpole board:
rvahams.com/hamapp/
Powerpole polarity tester:
www.w6trw.com/misc_ documentation_articles/anderson_powerpole_ tester/anderson_ power_pole_tester.pdf
Powerwerx (Powerpole accessories):
powerwerx.com
QuickSilver Radio (Powerpole accessories):
www.qsradio.com

Solar Battery Charge Controller by KIØBK:
ki0bk.no-ip.com/~pwrgate/LLPG/Site/Solar.html
Solar System Presentation by Jeremy, KF7IJZ:
youtu.be/8SuvAKZt0Vs
TG Electronics:
stores.tgelectronics.org
TSA regulations concerning batteries:
www.tsa.gov/travel/security-screening/whatcanibring/
West Mountain Radio:
www.westmountainradio.com
Wire and fusing size tables:
assets.bluesea.com/ les/resources/reference/20010.pdf

Weather and Propagation

APRS to SMS:
smsgte.wixsite.com/smsgte
APRS2SOTA:
www.sotaspots.co.uk
ARLHS BeaconBot:
arlhs.com/beacon-bot/
ARRL Propagation:
www.arrl.org/propagation-of-rf-signals
ARRL propagation web page:
www.arrl.org/propagation
ARRL — What the Numbers Mean:
www.arrl.org/the-sun-the-earth-the-ionosphere
Band Conditions:
www.bandconditions.com
BeaconAid-HF App:
itunes. apple.com/us/app/beaconaid-hf/ id307460004?mt=8
Comcast HotSpot:
wifi.xfinity.com/faq.php
DXheat:
dxheat.com/dxc/
DX Maps:
www.dxmaps.com/spots/mapg.php
DXplorer:
www.dxplorer.net
DXsummit:
www.dxsummit.fi

DXscape:
   www.dxscape.com
DX Watch:
   dxwatch.com
Facebook (post via text):
   www.facebook.com/help/170960386370271?helpref=faq_content
Garmin InReach:
   explore.garmin. com/en-US/inreach
HamAlert:
   hamalert.org/login
HamSpots:
   hamspots.net
Hurricane Watch Net:
   www.hwn.org   •
Make More Miles on VHF (VHF Beacon Map):
   www.mmmonvhf.de/bcn_map.php
NØHBH Propagation Tools and Solar Data:
   www.hamqsl.com/solar3.html
National Institute of Standards and Technology (NIST):
   www.nist.gov/pml/time-and-frequency-division/radio-stations
National Weather Service:
   www.weather.gov
NCDXF Beacon App:
   play.google.com/store/apps/ details?id=com.wolphi. clock&hl=en
NCDXF/IARU International Beacon Project:
   www.ncdxf.org/beacon/beaconprograms.html
NOAA Space Weather Prediction Center:
   www.swpc.noaa.gov/communities/radio-communications
Passage Weather:
   www.passageweather.com
PiGate:
   www.pigate.net
PredictWind:
   www.predictwind.com/why-predictwind-forecast
Propagation and Radio Science by Eric Nichols, KL7AJ, published by ARRL:
   www.arrl.org/shop/
PSKreporter:
   pskreporter.info
QSO Map:
   www.qsomap.org
Real Time DX HF Propagation Prediction (ON4AA):
   hamwaves.com/propagation.prediction/en/index.html

Reverse Beacon Network:
   www.reversebeacon.net
RF Propagation Analytics:
   dxdisplay.caps.ua.edu
SOTAwatch:
   www.sotawatch.org
Space Weather Woman:
   www.spaceweatherwoman.com
Stringify:
   www.stringify.com
The Watchers:
   watchers.news/category/geomagnetic-storms
Twitter (via text):
   help.twitter.com/en/using-twitter/twitter-sms-faqs
Ventusky:
   www.ventusky.com
VHF propagation maps:
   aprs.mountainlake.k12.mn.us
W6RK County Hunter's page:
   ch.w6rk.com
Weather fax:
   www.nws.noaa.gov/os/marine/radiofax.htm
WebSDR:
   www.websdr.org
Windy:
   www.windy.com
Winlink:
   winlink.org
Worldwide Tropospheric Ducting Forecast:
   www.dxinfocentre.com/tropo_wam.html
WSPR or Weak Signal Propagation Reporter:
   wsprnet.org/drupal/
WSPRLITE:
   www.sotabeams.co.uk
WWFFwatch:
   wwff.co/dx-cluster/
Wx2Inreach:
   wx2inreach.weebly.com

Index

The letters "ff" after a page number indicate coverage of the indexed topic on succeeding pages.

Notes

Notes